Lyndon Jeremiah

Memoirs

of

Nobody Important

First published in 2023 by Jeremiah Publishing 2021

ISBN: 978 1 8382713 6 7

A CIP record for this title is available from the British Library.

Text copyright © Lyndon Jeremiah

Illustrations copyright © Paula Parish

Cover Design by Nathan Shelton

Cover photograph by Simon Matthews

Edited by Rebecca Estano

Lyndon Jeremiah asserts his moral right under the Copyright, Designs and Patents Act, 1988 to be identified as the author of this work.

All rights reserved. No part of this book may be reproduced, stored in a retrieval system, traced in any form or by any means, electronic, electrostatic, magnetic tape, mechanical, photocopy, recording or otherwise without permission in writing from the above publishers.

JEREMIAH PUBLISHING
www.jeremiahpublishing.co.uk

Dedications

To my Megs,

Loving you is forever.

And yes, I will do it now, in a minute. X

Contents

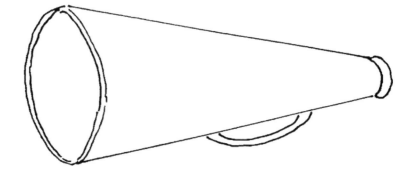

Introduction

So, let me get this off my chest from the get-go. Choosing the title of this book was the most difficult part of writing it. It will probably be my only book of short stories.

As I wrote that last sentence, I had a cinematic flash of hordes of teenage girls, divorced ladies with their mortgage paid off and the world's greatest literary critics, storming my palatial home, bought from the proceeds of my first collection of shorts stories, baying and pleading with me to release my second collection. With that in mind, you will, in this collection, read tales of my hopeless optimism, unrelenting positivity in the face of disparity and an undeserved confidence that, "God only knows," came from.

My interest in writing started in my teenage years or maybe it was an interest in something else?

Picture this: a fourteen-year-old me, sitting in my English lesson at Llangatwg Comprehensive in West Glamorgan in the South Wales valleys circa 1982. At the front of the class was my English teacher, Miss Jean Foulkes. Miss Jean Foulkes.

That is not an editorial mistake, I wanted to write it twice, for dramatic effect. Miss Jean Foulkes (that is three times) was the love of my short, and some might say, uneventful life. I remember the moment I fell hopelessly in love with her. I can pinpoint it to the nearest second. It was a laugh she did, a giggle really. A giggle that I had induced, made, manufactured or honed from a slab of comedy granite.

I was aware of the similarity of her name with Miss Jean Brodie, the main character in "The Prime of Miss Jean Brodie", a brilliant film I had watched with my Mam. Not my mother, my Mam's Mam, on a rainy Sunday.

1

I had unexpectedly loved it, mostly because of the wonderful Maggie Smith, who played the Scottish Miss Brodie, a teacher at a posh girl's school, with aplomb.

In the film, Maggie Smith refers to the Gurlls (that is how she pronounced girls) as the "Crème de la Crème". I liked that; it sounded great. It suited how I spoke, with my valley boy accent, rolling my Rs like I might never get a chance to roll them again. Rrright up my strreet. I did not really understand it, but I knew it was a "bit of French". It had become the most celebrated quote from the film.

In our English class, we were given the freedom to discuss topics that I would have been torn apart for in my other two domains of any modicum of success, the woodwork room and the rugby changing room. Janet Lloyd had raised the topic of the film in our lesson, which had irked me at first. Janet was my intellectual superior. Quite honestly, I was not in her league. Her and Wyn Griffiths were the only ones in 4C that I knew were clever, not hardworking clever, not the sort of clever that would ever be reflected in exam results, though they would end up with plenty of those.

They had an intellect that already, at fourteen, had broken free of the classroom and flew effortlessly through the skies of possibility of which I could only dream. Friends of mine to this day, they would be my "phone a friend" even if I did accidentally strike up a friendship with Stephen Fry or Professor Brian Cox. But I was funny, at least I genuinely believed I was.

I had used this as a smoke screen many times in their company to deflect my shortfall in knowledge and real intelligence to try to keep up.

They knew, they always knew, but as well as intellect they also possessed kindness. In a 1980's Welsh Comprehensive School, this was rare. Probably a sign of intelligence. Damn them both!

The conversation about "The Prime of Miss Jean Brodie" developed. It was only a matter of time before Miss Jean Foulkes (four times) had referred to us, her top stream English class, as her "Crème de la Crème."

This was my moment. Like all things that I have said at times in my life that I pompously reminisce upon, I am not sure where it came from, maybe a gift from the literary gods or just the efforts of an obsessed, over-hormonal kiss-arse who was desperate to please. "I think you'll find that we are the Phlegm de la Phlegm, Miss." I said in a mocking Scottish lady's voice and a confidence that surprised even me. There was a large smile from Janet, as she continued her notes; she always took notes. My next glance was to Wyn who was nodding in appreciation of my clever quip, with a downturned mouth and raised eyebrows. The complete bewildered silence from the rest of the class was broken only by a childlike squeal of delight, that quickly changed to a giggle, which is what it was, a simple giggle from Miss Jean Foulkes (I've started so I'll finish. Five) She stood and giggled, she sat and giggled. She just giggled. That was the moment I fell in love with um… writing.

You, by now, will have noticed my addiction to digression. Sorry, I have lots to say, and it doesn't all turn up at the right moment or necessarily in the right order. (Thanks, Eric. I loved Eric Morecambe).

Miss Jean Foulkes, (I'm over her), introduced me to Dylan Thomas. Not an earth-shattering revelation. He was the lifeblood of all English lessons in my school era and area and hopefully still is.

Oh, I hope so.

We also did Ted Hughes and Philip Larkin. They didn't interest me at all. Reading their poetry, to me, was like listening to two boring adults on a train talking about lives I would never have and situations I would never want to ever contemplate.

I've since changed my mind on Ted Hughes.

Be off with ya, Larkin.

"Fern Hill", "And death shall have no dominion" and "Do not go gentle into that good night" all became a staple diet of my fascination for Dylan, and I got it, I really got it, but it wasn't his poetry that snared me, it was his short stories.

Poetry-wise, I had much more genius to feast upon. God himself Max Boyce, Benny Hill, Spike Milligan, Mike Harding, Pam Ayres, Jasper Carrot, Bernard Cribbins, Ryan Davies, Victoria Wood, Billy Connolly and Ronnie Barker.

This was the verse that I found hard not to love. Basically, because it had one objective, laughter, my drug of choice.

But prose, by Dylan Thomas, his short stories in fact, were something that lit a fire in me that was to, not burn exactly, but glow gently for the next thirty-five years of my life.

"Portrait of the Artist as a Young Dog".

When I read this book for the first time, it didn't change my life, but it made it just a little bit better. I was an avid reader from an early age, but these were "boys own" adventures like "Robinson Crusoe", "Kidnapped" and "Treasure Island". I'd devoured Enid Blyton, (yes, I too just imagined chomping down on the thigh bone of an elderly but true literary pioneer), moved on to HG Wells, Alexandre Dumas and Ian Fleming. When I read "Portrait of the Artist as a Young Dog", it was the first time I felt I was reading something from the adult world, an insight maybe, into what was to come and what had been. It was the first time that I had read something where the place names were familiar to me, the characters had names like the people in my village, nicknames structured in the same way.

They behaved in ways I could relate to, and I saw their fears, anxieties and bravado in people I saw, loved and even hated every day.

The language was familiar, the phrases, the cynicism and the cutting remarks, the warm glow of love and the arse-smacking put downs. Even though it was written fifty years prior to my first reading, it was fresh to me, rude, hilarious and enlightening. Dylan had chosen the title as part tribute, part put down of James Joyce's "Portrait of the Artist as a Young Man". This did not go down well with everyone and hampered its success initially, but I loved that. I enjoyed the irreverence of it. Cheeky sod.

"The title of the book?" I hear you say, "Get back to that." I will.

I have always had an obsession with fatherhood. Both as a poorly served recipient and a naive purveyor. Fatherhood is the greatest of gifts. Some long for it but are, sadly, never blessed. Some have it thrust upon them and do magnificently. Others throw it away like a used betting slip or the phone number of a "ten-pound tart", (my Mam's phrase, not mine).

I have had huge triumphs and monumental failures. Moments that fill me with unmeasurable pride and times of guilt beyond measure. I have basked in its glory and shed the tears of thunderous inadequacies. One day, I hope to get it right or make it right.

With the lack of any structured patriarchal guidance, from an early age I had tried to make an impossible picture of fatherhood from the discarded remnants of a thousand jigsaw puzzles. I would dissect and dismember parts of fathers, grandfathers, uncles and just about any bloke that had shown me even a modicum of kindness, guidance or favour and stitch together a perfect specimen in the laboratory of my mind. Simply throw the switch, sending millions of volts through its lifeless body, bringing him instantly to life. Hey, Dad.

Like Mary Shelly and Victor Frankenstein before me I imagined that this would be a pretty good idea. Mary sold lots of books, of course, but for Victor it went a bit "tits up."

A huge fan of classic literature and sci -fi though I may be, I didn't want to create the monster, I wanted to be the monster. Well not a monster exactly, but you get my drift.

Television had always served up an opportunity to dream.

Back then, if I had to choose my top five TV Dads to mix into one delicious Super Dad it would have been Charles Ingles from "Little House on the Prairie", with a splash of Ben Cartwright from "Bonanza", a dollop of John Walton from "The Waltons", a pinch of Howard Cunningham from "Happy Days" and finishing off with a large helping of Bill Cosby from "The Cosby Show". Due, however, to recent events regarding Bill, I would have to bring Herman Munster from "The Munsters" off the subs bench, which I think rounds this analogy off rather nicely.

I didn't mean these stories to have such an undercurrent, to give my subconscious views on what it is to be a good father, it just happened. My initial outset was just to honestly, with hopefully a smattering of humour, give a perspective of what it was like to grow up in the 1970's on a Council Estate in rural South Wales and then to start to make my way in the world. I hope I have done this. I flirted with calling the book "Land of my Fathers", but quickly shied away from the threat of exploiting the stereotypical and overdone angle of "Proud Welshman writes a book."

Reading this book will convince you of my undeniable love for the country of my birth. This, alone, however, does not truly define me, it is not entirely who I am. I have therefore decided on "Fathers Land."

I hope you find a joyous shared experience in parts of this book. There are some parts of it, however, that I sincerely hope you have no experience of whatsoever.

Lyndon Jeremiah

Note to Reader - *Referral to the Glossary at the rear of this book may enhance the experience of these Memoirs.*

Medals of Mediocrity

I never realised, as a child, that I liked writing. I knew I liked words; words fascinated me. I loved words that seemed to create a reaction, whether they were on the television, radio or long-playing records. I used to sit there watching TV and a word I didn't understand caused outrage, sadness or, even better, laughter. I would rush to look up the word in my Collins dictionary. This resulted in me using some language early on that was, let's just say, unusual coming from a small boy. Most of the time, I got away with it. My Mam used to glow with pride when other Mams used to say, "Doesn't he speak nicely, " or "He's a clever boy, Ange," usually followed by, a little more quietly, "Unlike his father." As I didn't know my father, I still took this as a positive. I took most remarks as a positive. I was a positive sort of lad. Some had described it as a sunny disposition.

There were times, however, that my rather maverick approach to language caught me out and made me look either silly or an odious little shit. There were a couple of occasions that I remember.

My Mam worked at Mrs French's village shop. Mrs French was posh; she was the poshest person in the village and seemed to talk like she was from an old black and white film from a lost afternoon. This seemed to also affect how my Mam spoke in her company.

I had recently, for some forgotten reason, seen a copy of "Confessions of Window Cleaner" on Betamax. I do not remember how, maybe in a pal's house when their parents were out but I had definitely seen it.

I remember Robin Askwith, the star of those seedy films, saying to a co-star about a sandwich he was eating, "This tastes like dog shit." I thought this was the funniest thing I had ever heard and promised myself that I would use this outstanding punchline at the next possible opportunity.

That phrase burned a hole in my brain for the next couple of days until I decided, today was the day. At the end of her shift on a Saturday, I always met my Mam at the shop to walk the fifty yards back home, mostly because I usually got 5p worth of penny sweets for my trouble.

Today, however, Mrs French handed me an out of date "Cadbury's Cream Egg" as a reward for my gallantry. These were the days when a "Cadbury's Cream Egg" was the size of your fist. Maybe they are now cost engineered or maybe I was smaller then, but it seemed that way. Upon unwrapping my prize, I noticed that the chocolate was discoloured in the way that chocolate used to discolour before they put all sorts of preservatives in. Undaunted, I bit into it not even noticing what a rare treat this was for me. I had bigger fish to fry. I remarked with an unbridled glee, "My God, Mrs French, this tastes like dog shit."

I waited for them both to fall about with laughter, ruffle my hair and tell me how hilarious I was.

There was silence, a deathly silence, the sort of silence that indicates you are in huge trouble. I looked first at Mrs French, whose eyes seemed to roll in her head like a devil-possessed slot machine. That vision alone was alarming but when I looked at my Mam, she was white, white with disbelief, embarrassment, anger and disappointment. I knew what was coming next. I remember being lifted by one arm off the ground and carried out of the shop.

The first blow was off centre, my Mam hadn't found her range yet, but she would. The second was perfect and found its mark dead centre, right on my rear end. I hadn't had time to adjust my breathing pattern yet and so this caused my lungs to empty of air, this made it more difficult to eat my Cream Egg which I was still endeavouring to do.

Then, with almost perfect symmetry and elegance of motion, I received a smack on my arse every time my feet hit the ground all the way home. It seemed longer than fifty yards.

At my front gate, my Mam seemed to tire. She let go of my hand and cupped hers to her face. I stood there just about to cry, not because of my throbbing backside or my possibly dislocated shoulder, but because my Mam was crying.

That I could never bear. Others had caused it, but never me. It was then I realised she wasn't crying but laughing, well, laughing and crying. She stood there and laughed until she could laugh no more. It was lap-grabbing laughter that caused her to stoop forward to stop the wee from coming out. When she had composed herself, she then bent down and gave me a cwtch, probably my life's favourite cwtch. My lasting memory was the laughter.

I always remembered the laughter.

Another time was in Catwg Primary School, at the age of about six, when we had an essay competition where we had to read a passage of our laboured creations in front of the class. After several attempts by my classmates of which I took no notice whatsoever, it was my turn.

As I launched into my story of underwater intrigue and danger, I could see that my essay had the same mind-numbing effect on my classmates that theirs had had on me. That was until the teacher, Mrs Jones, or Popeye as she was known because she seemed to have one eye larger than the other, stopped me and asked me to repeat the last sentence, which I did.

Without any expression on her face Mrs Jones said, "Just pause there a moment Lyndon," and she then swiftly left the classroom. Upon return, she had Mr "Fuzzy" Williams with her, the teacher from the class next door. "Please read that for Mr Williams, Lyndon," she said, again with no visible reaction. Spurred on by this obvious endorsement of my prose, I re-read the section. This unexplainably caused Fuzzy to have a coughing fit and he left the room rather hurriedly, only to return almost immediately with Mr "Snoz" Davies.

The event was repeated and at the end of my masterpiece the three, Popeye, Fuzzy and Snoz, excused themselves into the corridor, to obviously discuss my literary future. What came next was very confusing indeed, as the corridor outside echoed with laughter. Raucous, wheezing laughter that I had only heard inside pubs or on Saturday nights watching "The Generation Game". I had a curious, awkward feeling all day and finally on my school bus trip home I decided to read my essay again, this time with my trusted Collins dictionary as adjudicator.

It didn't take me long to realise the true turn of events that day. When I had described the diver fighting for his life against the giant octopus, when he had wrapped his tentacles around his neck, I had used the word "testicles" instead. It now all made sense, the whole thing.

As I sat there on the "Ken Hopkins" bus on my short journey home, I remember smiling to myself.

I was smiling about the laughter I had unwittingly created. I only cared about the laughter.

 Laughter was important to me.

I loved school, almost everything about it. The order and the chaos. The structure and the carefree abandon. It was just like homelife to me, with the same mix of safety and spontaneity but without the flashes of sickening violence, but I'll get to that later.

School was for me, only me. I sat in lessons thinking that every word, every song and even the tales of moral guidance were there to mould and benefit me only. I flourished, excelled at times, and liked everyone and everyone liked me.

I wasn't strange looking, and I wasn't overweight, my clothes didn't smell stale from second hand smoke and neglect, and dinner tickets kept me fed and watered. I was out of breath from unbridled fun at least a dozen times a day. Life was good.

Our school was in the next village, but it could have been a different world away. Cadoxton was where the posh people lived, "the Crachach" as my Mam's Mam used to say. I now know this to mean a perceived Welsh-speaking elite but to me, back then, it was the kids who had two parents, their dad had a job, probably a car and the rent man would never darken their door.

My village was different, due mostly to the council estate right in the middle of it. My estate.

Until primary school, I hadn't realised there was a difference between us and them. I never knew that "Green Flash" daps were out of vogue, that bog standard football shirts from the "Kays Catalogue" were regarded as ammunition for ridicule or that my sister's white, elasticated second-hand school socks dyed black, well purple, were not a satisfactory replacement for school rugby socks. These were hard lessons to learn but we were tough from Cilfrew. Life had not dealt us the cards of a middle-class game of "Happy Families", so we just played council house "Snap", a game that needed a tough exterior, the ability to survive by learned behaviour and befriending your "enemies". Some were better at this than others, mere Jacks or Knaves, but I was the King.

After a while there seemed to be no difference between me and them, maybe it was true or more likely I was good at what I did. It didn't really matter, I loved school. I loved school so much that I never missed a day, not one. I mean it, not a single day. By the time I had reached the final year I was close to creating history in the school. Well, me and Nev Griffiths, that is. From the very start of primary school, attendance had been recognised as a measure of your success, your stamina, your ability to be like everyone else, better than everyone else. The first year of full attendance you got a bronze medal; a nice one, one that a World War One soldier could have lost a couple of fingers for in the trenches, shot off by the Hun of bad attendance and cosy days off with chicken soup and a John Wayne film.

The second year was a silver medal.

Bigger, shinier and a prize to behold, like a silver dollar awarded by the Lone Ranger that could be melted down to make silver bullets to kill Comanches or a rogue werewolf looking for scraps. By the third year only three of us remained: Me, Nev and Sean Ricketts. Sean was stoic in opposition, steady and quiet, plus his Nan was a dinner lady, a huge advantage. It was like he had his attendance coach in his corner every day, checking his temperature, wiping his nose, flapping the towel of endurance in his face between rounds. Sean's downfall was to be an unexpected nemesis, a figure of mystery and feared throughout the school: Mrs Pugh, the nit nurse. She sent him home one Thursday afternoon with a small group of celebrating minions who punched the air at the thought of a few days off. Sean was devastated, old Mrs Ricketts was incandescent with rage. A face off took place that day that is still talked about today.

Old Mrs Ricketts and Mrs Pugh the nit nurse. The unstoppable force and the immovable object, in the yard, in the open and in the gutter. I only remember one thing that was said, the last thing. What preceded it was the posturing, the grimacing, the folded arms under their considerably fearsome bosoms.

The quivering lips of anger, the accusations back and forth, the humiliation and the pride. Mrs Pugh had the moral high ground, the better position in the school, an infrequent visitor with less to lose, and she wasn't going to lose. Old Mrs Ricketts was on the ropes. It was Ali versus Foreman, it was the "Rumble at the Jumble," there was no possible way back. She did the only thing left at her disposal: personal insults.

The last retort, from Sean's Nan, was simple, to the point and ultimately vicious in content and caused the whole community to take an audible intake of breath that was to last for years to come.

"And anyway," said old Mrs Ricketts, "Dai Roundabout saw your husband with his fancy piece in the "The Bluebell" and she had mud on her tights."

With that, she left the school, never to return. Sean left with her that day knowing he was out of the race forever. He looked back at me from the school gates, he smiled with a generous resignation that, I'd like to think, was a good luck gesture to go forth and claim my destiny.

I said I was a positive sort of lad.

The smile ended abruptly like a scratched record as Sean received a heavy-handed slap around the head for dawdling. She was not a happy Nan.

Nev and I received our gold medals at the end of the third year at primary school, awarded by Dr Sykes, or Cyclops, as he was known, the headmaster, who seemed to me, at the time, to be the tallest man in the world with hands like car seats. By this time, only the two of us cared about it, except for our Mams. Nev's Mam was nice, like my Mam. But she drove a car, no less, a real car of her own, not shared even with Nev's Dad. This gave him a huge advantage in our quest to become the only person to attend Catwg Primary School for five years without a single absence.

Early dentist appointments meant he could be back at the gates before school, with his Mam dropping him off.

Doctor's appointments after school, for his growing pains (Nev was nearly six feet when we went to big school) were also carefully managed. I had to go to the dentist on a Saturday morning or worse, in the holidays, to work such miracles.

Nev also lived a stone's throw from the school and would easily be home for "Jackanory" whereas I had a bus journey and a five-minute walk to contend with. I had calculated that with my journey to and from school considered, I had already attended school for three months longer than Nev.

You can tell by this ridiculous statement that this meant a great deal to me.

Year four came and went with no major setbacks on the attendance front with only one minor blip. I had had a rather disastrous haircut one Saturday morning. Well, it was half a haircut really. My Mam and my Auntie Glo had left me and my cousin Steffan at the barbers at the back of the market. The queue was massive, so they went and did some shopping whilst we waited our turn.

He was a big lad, Steff, friendly and gentle. I had never seen him react in any other way than to nod quietly or to smile obligingly. Ours was not a gregarious friendship but he was my cousin. I was very surprised to see his reaction that unique Saturday morning. We were both in the chairs alongside each other, engulfed in the barber's cloaks, our hair combed flat so that we were reminiscent of two "Playmobil" men in the executioner's chair. Within minutes, one side of my hair was completed, it was neater, shorter and half of the same haircut I'd had for the last five years.

Then it happened. There was an almighty scream from Steff, a scream so piercing and animalistic that, at first, I didn't realise it was him. He jumped from the chair and started to run around the room like a rat in a basket. He was shouting "No, no, no, not again, she's going to kill me, not again, please." I'd never seen him in this light before or operate at such a heightened pace. He was at double speed, wailing and crying, talking to himself, trying to reassure himself that all would be ok. Then I saw the blood, it wasn't much, dripping onto the gown he was wearing.

He had no arms on view and appeared, to me, to be a bit like a very large, agitated "Walnut Whip". Dave, the barber, tried to take charge of the escalating situation.

Dave was a man of the times. Slim of waist, blonde, with a hair share agreement with Noel Edmonds.

He was a ladies' man and would turn my Mam into a giggling schoolgirl that blushed profusely and scurried like a grain store mouse.

"Sit down son, it's only a nick," said Dave through his very extravagant moustache. I then realised what had taken place. The other barber, a trainee, had cut a small slice in Steff's ear. There was nothing missing, more of a little flap than anything. But, by God, it was bleeding now.

Several punters up and left immediately. I remember thinking that the queue wasn't so bad now and quiet for a Saturday. "Come here son, let me take a look," said Dave.

"No," said Steff, "I need an ambulance, I need it now," the blood now running visibly down his neck, his hands were covered and there were bloody handprints wherever he had been.

It was like the Hammer House of Haircuts. The trainee was then sick into the sinks where you get your hair washed, which was surprisingly a perfect shape for vomiting into, as it fitted his convulsing throat perfectly.

"I'm not calling an ambulance for a bloody nick on the ear," Dave remonstrated. (Which I thought was amusing, it being "bloody" and all that.) "We'll soon get that sorted with a plaster, come here."

"Well, you'd better call one!" screamed Steff. "I'm a Haemophiliac."

Homo-Feely-Yak? Nope. I'd run it through my restricted database, and I could not for the life of me find a suitable match. Unless of course Steff was admitting to being a rather amorous form of cattle living an alternative lifestyle somewhere in Tibet. I snapped out of my daydream. Upon hearing Steff's plea, Dave went visibly ashen and ran out of the room immediately, leaving me and the trainee, with diced carrots on his chin, in charge.

Before I had a chance to save the day from whatever the dire situation was, he was back, with Ivor the St John's ambulance man from the market next door. Ivor was well known around the town as he attended all the Neath RFC matches. The situation was surely saved. It is worth noting that, for no other reason than it is the truth, Ivor was a Dwarf and had a clubbed foot.

He was brilliant, he opened the box I had seen him struggle to carry to the halfway line on many occasions but never revealed its contents. Steff was a huge Neath RFC fan and hardly missed a home game. For a moment, he was visibly in awe of the fact he was in the presence of a minor celebrity.

Minor as in his status in a small Welsh town, not minor as in his stature. The inside of Ivor's medical box was a sheer marvel.

It smelt of liniment and love, the joy of away wins and the disappointment of going out of the cup to Llanelli at the Gnoll ground. His unusually high-pitched voice was instantly calming to both me and Steff as Ivor amazed us all with his dexterity and crisis management. Within minutes, Steff was back in the chair, with a compressed towel held in place and, for now at least, the blood had stopped.

Moments later the ambulance arrived, and Steff was whisked away to make a full recovery after an over theatrical break from school. Oh, the irony. Ivor meticulously replaced his equipment in his box and shut the lid made of plywood and painted in the Neath colours of black with white. Painted on the front in bold letters was "NEATH RFc", there was not enough room left, by the obviously inexperienced calligrapher, for a capital "C". It's strange what you remember.

All I had to do was find my Mam and Auntie Glo in the market, with my half a haircut and break it to them gently, or overdramatically, as I'm sure you've realised is my way.

Auntie Glo came over all funny and Frank from the butchers, an old flame, took her straight to the hospital, but only after bagging up her lamb's liver and belly pork then spitting into the sawdust on the floor and removing his apron. For reasons only known to him, he kept on his straw boater.

We did go back for the other half of my haircut, but Dave's Salon was shut.

No doubt, he was finding solace at one of the many watering holes in the town at which he was a frequent visitor. His moustache coated in froth as he entertained the ladies of the afternoon with tales of the Demon Barber of Neath. My Auntie Wendy finished my haircut. She was more accustomed to coiffuring ladies of a certain age, so I rather reluctantly attended school that following Monday with one half of my head looking like a Bay City Roller and the other half resembling Farrah Fawcett from "Charlie's Angels".

I was, however, there on that Monday and still on track. The record was still on. The award that year was a trophy of sorts. It took the form of a fake fountain pen in gold plastic on a curled page, also in plastic, in turn mounted on a small piece of mahogany. I instantly thought or have remembered since, I'm not sure which, that it was reminiscent of a "Blankety Blank Chequebook and Pen", awarded by Terry Wogan with his microphone wand and his blankety blarney, instead of something worthwhile, that people could really use.

This year it had our names on it, one each. This was the big time.

So Nev and I turned up that September to make history, to go where no Catwg School pre-pubescent had gone before. We were already legends.

In our own minds at least.

Four years full attendance meant we had taken the record of three years and forty six days from Mavis Davis, a name from the ancient past of 1964 on the role of honour board that had driven us forward for all those dark winter months when all you wanted to do was cwtch up in bed of a morning and spend the day listening to your Mam and her co-conspirators ruin the fine reputations of everyone in the village, with "Trumpton" at lunchtime. Toothache, flu or nits couldn't stop us now.

The last year at Primary School went as planned. The Christmas concert came and went. I didn't make the cut for the school choir. Mrs Lewis' grimace on hearing my solo piece put pay to that and I had to suffer the humiliation of carrying the benches on and off the stage with Peter Sparkes and Mark Davies, two boys so entirely void of a moral compass that I once saw them steal the "Sunblest" bag on the dashboard of the school bus that contained the sandwiches of Jacko the driver.

They later threw them at each other because they were made from brown bread and therefore poisonous. Undaunted by my demotion to stagehand, I carried on through the school year regardless. The Easter Bunny and St David ambled nostalgically, hand in hand, through our school year with leek flavoured eggs and dragon shaped bonnets. April the 1st saw Fuzzy Williams find it hilarious to discover an imitation turd in his Monday morning bin.

His reaction when he reached inside to find that it was not, in fact, an imposter was something that all of us would spend many years wishing we had never seen. And so, the summer term was upon us.

The smell of freshly mown grass and games of "Murderball" were the lasting memories, interspersed with my first kiss and my first broken heart.

Both happened in the same lunchtime, and I was over it in time for the bus.

I loved that last summer in Catwg Primary School. No older kids to steal your bus seat, just the warmth of familiarity, the comfort of friendship and a complete insulation from how mean life could really be. I never thought about the attendance record; that was in the bag, neither of us would slip up now.

Nev and I knew we had a really great day to look forward to, the best of days, to reward our hard work and our stubbornness, our strive for perfection. We were a team. We were "Starsky and Hutch", "Bodie and Doyle," we were Nev and Lynd, winners of the trophy for five years of full attendance. Never been done before, never to be repeated. There was only one trophy in the cabinet outside Dr Sykes office.

Big, golden with dragonesque handles and a brown Bakelite base. Worthy of Le Mans, of the Five Nations Championship or the Urdd Eisteddfod, and soon it would be ours, one each.

The other must have been in Dr Sykes drawer, in his desk, with his whiskey and "Woodbines". I never gave it another thought.

The last chill of April gave way to the promise of May as we rounded the final corner to June. It was a better than ordinary time; my stepfather had buggered off again, for six weeks this time, and home was a place where I could be as happy as school, happier even. Ham was replaced with corned beef and seconds became a rarity. Evenings were made up of dusky games of football or jumping ramps on our bikes up until the streetlamps came on, then in and bath if it was a Sunday, flannel wash if not, tea and toast and "On the Buses" before bed.

The next day was a well-oiled routine, same old. Up, brush my teeth, brush my hair, pick the sleep gravel from the corners of my eyes, fried Spam or Weetabix, never both, check my satchel and out the door. There was no difference, apart from one thing.

As I came into the kitchen to receive my cwtch of mild tobacco and bleach, my Mam was nowhere to be found. Undaunted, I turned to leave.

Then a whisper, "Lyndon," my Mam's voice. "Lynd, come here," it continued. I looked down to see my Mam behind the couch in front of the window. "Sshh," she said, "Get in here."

I had absolutely no idea what was going on. Maybe a trick on my Auntie Iona, who sometimes popped in early doors to stop my Mam cleaning or maybe she had found the rotting carcass of the school hamster I had lost the year before, during its summer evacuation when I was playing Evel Knievel with it, off the windowsill onto the couch cushions.

Reacting to the urgency in her voice, I slid in beside her. "What's going on?" I spoke. "Sshh, he'll hear you," came the whispered reply. So, we lay there, for just moments really, before I realised her reasoning. The silence was decimated by the door knocker. A friendly rhythmic introduction to the day. Followed a minute later by the exact same rhythm with more tempo. I looked at my Mam from close quarters, closer than I had for a while, realising that I hadn't been so close to her for a couple of years, not since I was much younger, when I was almost part of her, never leaving her side. I had a yearning to be younger again, to not have to ever grow older.

The door knocker was given its marching orders in favour of a thumping of the door. Three times, followed by two more. "Mrs Regan, are you there?" came the opening line to what was quickly becoming the "Play for Today."

I hated the name Regan, it wasn't mine. It was my mother's and my brothers', but it wasn't mine. "It's Mr Pike, Mrs Regan, from the council, to collect the rent." I'd seen "Old Pikey" before, he collected once a month but occasionally he came round on a Saturday to other houses, never mine, to catch out the dodgers or to rob the Friday pay packets of the employed.

I never knew he came to my house. Whilst this was filtering into my addled consciousness, he appeared at the net curtains in the kitchen. His face was wrinkled, as his hand, on his forehead, tried to improve his spectacled vision into the house. "Mam," I gently said, quieter than I had ever spoken before. "The bus, Mam, I've missed the bus."

Pikey's face gave one more visit to the window, like a hapless, moustache-less Hitler, pressed his nose on the glass, his dark greasy hair swept from right to left, his leather, embossed, zippered briefcase resting against his chin, then he was gone. Silence ensued until the end of the second act reached a crescendo with the clang of the garden gate. "I've missed the bus, Mam." I repeated. She didn't look at me, she didn't speak. She pulled my head tenderly to hers and cried.

I knew she wasn't crying about Pikey or the rent or her useless bastard husband or the hardness of her life or constant grind to keep us all fed and happy. She was crying because she thought she had let me down. She felt she had failed me by not catching the bus, by not getting the record and by not being as good as the rest of them. We stayed behind the couch for what seemed a short time but was much longer. It was safe there. A place away from the world.

The stupid medals, the rent, the Friday night shouting and the flicks around the ear, the arm pinching and the backhanders.

Mam got out from behind there first. I stayed. I didn't feel sad, there was no hole in my life from the accolades and silverware. If anything, there was a lifting of responsibility, a release of the non-important. Two cups of tea on a tray with mint Viscounts appeared at the front of my cave of non-attendance. "Move over my boy," said Mam. We pulled out the couch further from the window and draped the crocheted blanket, from under the stairs, over the back of the couch, weighted down on the windowsill with ornaments and bags of flour from the pantry. She laid the tray down and settled beside me. We spent all morning there.

21

There was toast with Welsh butter, fizzy Corona and Penguins. She told me about her school days, when the farmer used to slaughter the pigs and the whole school had the afternoon off to watch. She talked about my Grandad Reg and his fishing and when he'd fixed a puncture with a postage stamp when riding over the mountains to meet my Mam's Mam, how we were related to Richard Burton and how, when she was a teenager, she looked like Anita Harris, off the telly. The day was not like a weekday, it wasn't like a weekend, Christmas, Easter, or the sing-along parties of the Jubilee. It was better, undefinable and glorious. I never wanted to leave our space behind the couch and in some ways I never did. I go back there occasionally, in my mind, and if I close my eyes and breathe slowly, I can smell the leatherette or feel the cold outside wall against the small of my back. I can see my mother with her storytelling smile, laughing, with her glasses moved to the end of her nose impersonating Old Pikey, the rent man.

I can still see the shapes of the sunlight through that multicoloured crocheted blanket, casting reflective diamonds across our moment in time.

I always remember the laughter.

Uncle Selwyn

The day began, drenched in a dream.

"Moist the plain sail ya seadog or I'll cut ya to pieces and feed ya to Jaws 2," snarled Cap'n Scab Davies of the Cilfrew Cutlass, the most feared pirate ship in the whole of Swansea Bay.

"Not if I get the varmint first," Black Dan the Braggard screamed. Sheep rustler, shoplifter, seller of cheap cigarettes and just about the quickest gun in the entire Neath valley. His chewing tobacco oozed through his badger-stained moustache. "I'll fill him full of holes like Auntie Annie's bloomers." Time was running out. Not only did I have to battle to certain death with both of my evil nemeses, but also, I had a desperate need to get to somewhere I could not remember whilst my teeth fell out and my trousers disappeared so that the girls of Catwg Primary School could see my willy.

Auntie Annie, knickers on her head, called out, "Lyndon... Lyndon... come on, my boy... " I could see her now, standing in her garden in Drummond Road, with her Sunday school smile with Uncle Roy and Elvis.

"Come on Lyndon, it's time to go." They turned to leave, off to Graceland or Edgecumbe in Cornwall to photograph flowers. The image was fading now. "Lyndon... Come on, Uncle Selwyn will be waiting." This last message from the high seas of The Mumbles or the dust plains of Merthyr brings in the day, the hazy torment as Saturday heroically ripped me from the evil grasp of Friday.

I stared at the stain on the ceiling, it still looked like Brian from "The Magic Roundabout"... bearings complete. "Lyndon, Uncle Selwyn will be bloody waiting." Mam calls up from the kitchen followed by the fishhook lure of weekend Yosemite Spam. I'm up, on my feet. Information floods into my brain.

"Coming Mam," I called down. I fought the temptation of wearing my "town" clothes straight away as I knew I would be right back up to change. Like a man tossing cabers in the porridge-covered highlands of Scotland, I went downstairs. Ignoring any further thought of oats, I sat at the table and inhaled my breakfast like the boys at school on dinner tickets, of which I was gladly one. Refuelling completed, I frisbeed my faded plastic plate into the bowl and made for the door. Standing in front of my daps but waiting for the call.

"Wellies," called my invisible, omnipresent Mother. "Mam, mun," I remonstrated.
"Don't you bloody Mam mun me. Put your wellies on," she droned. "Bloody, shitting wellies," I said, loud enough so the cat could hear. I had spent the whole summer in my wellies. I loved my wellies, my old wellies. My old wellies that Bryn put a knife through when playing splitsies down the rec. It was close enough to draw the blood of a hero but not enough to warrant running home to Mam in the full bawl of a banshee. Mam's replacement wellies were typical of her. More expensive but an utter disgrace. Upon seeing them I immediately planned their demise. My old wellies had given me the "Bull Ring Boys" ring around the top of my legs, a mark of solidarity that was sore for a day or so at the beginning of the summer but then worn with pride for the rest of it. Now I would have two rings and not fit in.

My new wellies were three quarter length and were red and yellow with handles on each, which were begrudgingly convenient, with yellow toe caps. Embarrassingly it had the word "Fire" on the right foot and "Chief" on the left. I slipped them on with hateful ease and left the house. Hop, skip, jump and I was in the next door's garden.

There was Uncle Selwyn. Sel to my Mam. Her uncle and mine. He had his back to me. I instantly felt the guilt of being late although I was on time.

He was big to me, broad and tall, though he described himself as "little and good, like a Welshman's cow". In his vest and braces, his "trowsus y tatws" and "gawd blimey boots" he remained facing away.

His bearskin back escaping its cotton confines only to be stopped in its tracks by the barber's blade, two inches lower than the crisp line of the start of his hair. Immaculately black and combed by a draughtsman, it tried hopelessly to persuade his comb over to sit down and behave. Auntie Betty had said, "God himself has the same problem."

"Morning Uncle Selwyn," I said, not expecting a response. "Lyndon." came the unrequired reply.

I knew the drill. I fetched the sacks from under the tin sheet, removed the half brick that secured them from the wind and got straight to work.

My knees felt cold and damp against the soil, but I felt safe in the knowledge that the stones had been removed over years of obsessive screening. As I got into position, I felt conscious of my brightly coloured wellies and tried for a brief moment to cover them with the second sack, which I found immediately impractical and dispensed with the futile attempt.

Uncle Selwyn had made a good start, an early morning sweat sat on his brow as he turned the soil with a dexterity that would be difficult to catch.

In front of me was the task at hand, dozens of smooth, dirty prisoners rescued from the incarceration of the ground, calling, regaling their freedom as I quickly scooped them from the earth.

I loved this job; I loved the fact that I alone could save Uncle Selwyn's back from the evils of bending down. I think he thought it was difficult for me too, but it wasn't.

Sure, I would theatrically make a lifting groan, like Mick McManus raising Kendo Nagasaki above his head before pile driving him into the canvas, when the sack was full, as I carried it to the end of the greenhouse, or over-egg the strain of pulling a particularly deep spud, but I enjoyed the thoroughness required, the order of leaving the soil dank and dark as it lightened in the early morning sun. I soon caught up but did not go too quickly to embarrass or harass his rhythm. Seed potatoes in the bucket and the roots on the compost heap as I filled the first bag with ease.

"Your Mam?" Was the question I had been waiting for. It came with an abruptness that others would have confused for irritation, but I knew it to be his way. "She's well, Uncle Selwyn, apart from her veins," I betrayed.

"Nasty business," said Uncle Selwyn as he closed that particular line of conversation down before any more dramatic secrets were revealed. "Your Mam's Mam?" came the even more predictable enquiry. "She's a bit better now and made some Welsh cakes." I tried enthusiastically to not repeat my answer from last week which had involved bara brith. "Too much cinnamon and she cleans her stone too often," came his less than gentlemanly retort.

Uncle Selwyn's Welsh cakes were regarded as the best in Cilfrew, but I couldn't tell the difference apart from the fact they were bigger, and he used currants. My Mam's Mam used sultanas. "Send her my love," he said with a genuine glimmer of affection. "I will," I said as this week's Q and A ended.

After that came the bulk of the work and within the hour there were four bulging sacks of the finest Maris Pipers ready to be mashed, smashed, chipped and roasted, with the peelings going to Jean, my goat. "A job done well is a job well done," brought proceedings to a close and Uncle Selwyn straightened his back for the first time that morning, interlocked his fingers and clicked them all like a gunslinger ready to kill.

He then whipped his comb over with the skill of a lion tamer and it fell perfectly into place. I washed my hands in an old tin bucket next to the carrots and wiped them on the seat of my shorts, the only part of me not soiled with soil.

A post work Woodbine was ignited and, reminiscent of a Chicago gangster, Uncle Selwyn filled his lungs with the satisfaction of good old graft or gunning down a rival Mob boss. "Right then, off to work," he concluded.

Uncle Selwyn worked every Saturday but went in mid-morning. He took the bus but never paid. He reached into his work trousers and, after much rummaging through his otherwise empty pocket, pulled out a shiny 50p.

"Don't tell your mother." He said with a narrowed glint as he spun the coin in my direction. I caught it with one hand and didn't drop it as I had done the previous Saturday, a skill I had practised all week.

He then broke protocol and ruffled my hair with his surprisingly un-calloused hands. He had never done this before and it gave me an instant lift, an unexpected, unfamiliar feeling of acknowledgement. The moment was fleeting but unforgettable, momentary yet memorable.

"Don't be late next week," he readjusted. "I never am," I said to myself silently as I vaulted the razor-sharp tin sheet that divided his garden and ours. Three strides and I was at our back door. Inside, I took off my dirty vest and shorts and put them in the magic bin, the bin that miraculously transformed my grubby play clothes into clean ones, ironed them and folded them neatly into my bedroom drawer. I had very little time: eight minutes to be at the bus stop.

Saturday was the greatest day, little Christmas every week. I was meeting Bryn, Will and Tommy Bach and we were off to Dyfed Road Baths, something we did every couple of Saturdays when we had scraped together enough funds to go.

My newfound employment had meant our current expedition was fully patronised. Previous times we had relied on Will's Mam winning the Bingo and Bryn nicking a pound note from his dad's trousers when he'd got home from the pub.

Bryn's dad was a bastard. I had never heard him speak but the bruises that Bryn wore regularly without comment or question meant we all hated his guts. Bryn ignored his existence when he was out of earshot, and we never encroached on his freedom in our company. Bryn's Dad died years later by falling down the cwm whilst on his way home from the pub. Some say he was pushed over the top by someone in the village, of which there were many suspects.

The Police did investigate but after the umpteenth potential murderer said the same thing, "If I'd have been there, I'd have pushed the bastard." They confirmed it as "death by misadventure".

Bryn's bruises faded for the last time.

The bus fare to Neath was fifteen pence each, return on the number 57. The swimming pool entry was thirty pence each for two hours and if we could manage it, we would share large chips and scalpings on the bench in Victoria Park whilst Tommy Bach tried to catch a pigeon with his bath towel. He never did catch one but watching him try was my favourite part of the day. Looking back, I think he knew this and making us laugh was of more importance than any fabled pigeon pie.

There we stood, the fearless four, small boys no more, adventure loomed, unheralded heroes waiting to be crowned. The bus passed us on the way to the turning then within minutes was pulling up at the stop in the resplendent red and gold of United Welsh Buses finest livery as it coughed to a stop. Gwyn was driving. We loved Gwyn. Gwyn was our favourite. If the bus was empty, he used to let us sit down at the front and he would ask about our Mams.

He was compact and strong with a chest like a water butt and a laugh like a well. His face smiled when it didn't mean to, and he reminded me of "Benny the Ball" from "Topcat." "I'm going to be your dad one day, boys," he would say.

"You're too fat for my Mam, Gwyn, she likes them skinny, like David Bowie," said Will. "Cheeky sod. Well, tell her I've got all my own hair and most of my own teeth," he vibrated with laughter. Secretly, I wished Gwyn was my dad.

We pulled into Neath, up Windsor Road and through Albert Street to Victoria Gardens. Town was exciting, the bustle of the brave.

Packed with "big shop" women struggling with blue fingers to carry supplies back to the troops whilst their husband watched rugby or football or had afternoon delight with a horse, only to be "Buckaroo' ed" in the balls. The henpecked husbands filed in neatly behind their commanding officer as she clucked and sniped him into line.

The bobbing and the weaving of the busy, the idle window-watchers passing away the time extravagantly, even though they had so little of it left.

The flat caps of the old and the bonnets of the soon to be. The men lighting woodbines in the street and the tutting of the disapproving widows as they eyed their next victims. Prams with Mams and the pushchairs of the unmarried. Insolent little boys getting away with murder whilst the innocent found the wrath of their grandmothers. Smells of the sea and the bake house floor, butchers with body parts from the fights last night arranged convincingly in rows. Women buying meat that could well be the husband it was meant for. Serves him right.

Neath was manicured and messy, elegant yet confused. Once a beautiful Victorian lady with ivory skin that held her own counsel, she now swaggered into the new decade with sailor bag trousers and oversized sunglasses.

She had lost her looks but the sexiness of the Seventies was all around, replacing the trusted drabness of the last century with resplendent colour and the temporariness of youth. We loved it.

"Look after those return tickets, boys," shouted Gwyn as we disembarked, swinging off the central pole of the bus like Chinese acrobats. "There's a new bloke on the afternoon shift and he's a bloody stickler." We waved and took no notice. Bryn mistimed his exit and crumpled into the bus stop sign. We laughed uncontrollably and ran in zig zags to Dyfed Road Baths. I felt inside my front pocket of my trousers for my ticket; it was still there.

Breathlessly, we arrived at the baths. The recovery time was instant, and we queued manically for entry. The vacating early swimmers with the lank-haired disregard for death exited neatly. "Make sure you dry your hair properly," barked my Mam that morning. "You'll catch pneumonia if you don't. The last thing I need is a funeral to pay for before Christmas." I looked on helplessly as the still moist bathers revolved out into the mild summer morning to their certain death, but I said nothing. The overbearing heat hit us straight in the lungs. The quarter mile assault course over bollards and bins, verges and viburnums had been the worst preparation for our subtropical playground. We longed to be unclothed, in our trunks that were rolled up in the washed-out towels under our arms. Towels that were on their last legs that could be deemed as collateral damage, were their unforgivable loss to happen. The smell of the baths was intoxicating. Chlorine, sweat, plasters and verrucae all competed for our attention. Bleach and botulism hid secretly around every corner as we finally pushed through the metal milking stool fixed confusingly on its side. Bryn got his pocket caught on the last revolve of the leg and ripped his Saturday trousers.

We rejoiced at this comedy gift and scrummed down into the changing rooms arm in arm, shoulder to shoulder.

Our exuberant entry was short lived as we came face to face with our worst nightmare, the Caerwern Crew. They didn't know us, but we knew them.

They were the sworn enemies of the older boys in our village. Tall, strong, and ugly with overbites and pimples, hairy armpits and pubes.

We instantly fell silent, but this made our initial entrance more noticeable. We turned left and found a corner to change into our bathers, but the red flag had been raised. In seconds they stood over us, the same in number but four years apart in age. "Where are you girls from?" said Overbite. "Cilfrew, I bet," said Armpits. "Cadoxton," said Bryn with a deceptive braveness that petered off noticeably. Cadoxton was neutral ground, non-threatening, with no axe to grind and no allegiance that threatened our safety, a bit like Switzerland.

I was turned away and used the moment to check my bus ticket. It was still in my pocket, safe. "You're in the wrong changing rooms," said Pimples, "Girls are next door," he continued. "Yes, I bet they've all got fannies. Go on, show us your fannies," said Pubes. This was our saving grace. Overbite turned angrily and slapped Pubes about the head and said, "I've told you Norm, don't speak. You're too fucking stupid to speak." "Sorry Dai," said Pubes. Without another word, they turned and headed for the pool, but not before snatching Tommy Bach's towel, unrolling it and giving me a nipple twister. The pain was excruciating but a small price to pay for our early release.

We sat despondent on the benches and slowly changed into our trunks in silence. The day was ruined. We could never have a great time now.

Will sat without moving, staring into a lost world of hatred and revenge. Will was the quietest of us all but the more likely to do something outrageous.

"Let it go, Will," I said, "See you in there." The three of us walked through the disinfectant foot wash and into the pool area.

We lingered on the side of the pool which was full of the great unwashed from all the villages around the Neath valley and tried to see where the Caerwern Crew had based themselves so we could spend the whole two hours avoiding them in the shallow end. We couldn't see them at all and at first thought they had already been expelled which probably happened often. It was then I noticed my dirty knees from my morning's toil and so without drawing attention to them I backed up and returned to the disinfectant and hurriedly knelt in the pinkness and scrubbed them clean. There was an enormous scream, a female scream, followed by a huge collective "OOH!!" by the whole of the swimming pool participants en masse. I rushed back in to see what the commotion was all about, Will was at my side as bewildered as me. "What happened?" said Will. Bryn and Tommy Bach stood in silence, unable to speak, ashen and open mouthed.

What had transpired and gone straight into local folklore and onto "The Neath Guardian" front page was that "The Crew" had gone straight to the second highest diving platform, the highest was closed and always had been. Egged on by the rest and eager to keep his position as leader, Overbite had jumped from the platform. This was not a great feat as all four of us had dived from there on many occasions, but it turned out Overbite couldn't swim.

He had tried to compensate for this by jumping closer to the side in the vain attempt to grab on to the side rail and avoid the eight-foot six-inch depth from swallowing him to an embarrassing flounder.

Unfortunately for him he had misjudged the stunt and caught his arm and formidable chin on the side of the pool, dislodging his dignity, his collarbone and eight of his teeth.

As we witnessed the aftermath, his unconscious body being carried away, the other three, now leaderless and timid, followed the stretcher as the ambulance pulled up to the emergency fire doors. All four with clothes in hand being bundled into the ambulance and awaiting Police cars.

The poolside was quickly hosed down to remove the blood and un-gathered teeth, then as if someone had flicked a switch, the cacophony of, nobody cared, noise started again immediately. I broke the silence amongst us first.

"I'm surprised he thought he would ever miss the side with a fucking chin that big." "They'll be picking out teeth from his brains down at the hospital," prophesied Bryn. "What fucking brains?" delighted Tommy Bach. We all looked at Will, for his contribution to the celebrations.

There was a pause, long but well worth the suspense when he finally announced, "I almost feel bad that I shit in his sock now." We fell about in uncontrolled laughter. We were back in the game, vindicated and victorious. What a moment. What a day. We swam, dive bombed and horse-played away the remainder of the two hours, ticking off nine of the ten things we were not allowed to do on the enamelled warning poster. We left the "heavy petting" for a future visit as we were a little unsure as to what it involved.

Back in the changing room we hurriedly dressed and excitedly chattered about telling the older boys in the village about our adventure that day, suitably embellished with tales of our bravery and contribution to the cause. We would leave out the bit about Cadoxton and the nipple twist, which was still sore and swollen. We had some added time onto our swim time because of Overbite's chin plant and so were a little late for the bus and so would have to miss out on our chips, but this was an acceptable compromise and so we bought four packets of "Space Raiders" from the pool shop on the way out instead.

I checked my bus ticket in my pocket, with my damp, chlorine-aged fingers before heading off, bus stop bound. It was still there, safe and sound.

We piggy backed and vaulted our way on the reverse journey back to Victoria Gardens, lost in the euphoria of our splendid day. We left the pool damp and clammy only to arrive at the bus stop dried by inertia and the summer's warm afternoon breeze.

The bus, already in, was a double decker, the jackpot, as rare as a "double yolker" or the day the ice cream van broke down in the village and Mr Whippy pulled free cones quicker than we could eat so his machine didn't get filled with melted gloop. This day was indeed glorious, we would talk of this day forever and raise a cow horn cup of ale in Valhalla or a cracked cup of tea at "old age" Tuesdays.

The downstairs was nearly full as I let the boys go first so I could get my ticket out of my pocket and finally relieve my stress of its ownership and hand it over. Bryn, Will and Tommy Bach disappeared up the dog-legged stairs like they were under the influence of a vacuum.

Then I noticed the new driver, unfamiliar and unfriendly. No chat with the regulars but he was new, so it was to be expected, I thought. I handed over my ticket and positioned my foot to hit the bottom step perfectly to get maximum spring to join the boys upstairs where we would sing "We are the Welsh", "Found some peanuts last night" and "My old man's a dustman", until we were told to stop.

"Not Valid," came the response. I didn't answer or ask for it to be repeated. "I can't read this ticket." I checked if he was speaking to me. I looked at the faces of the people on the bus, looking out of the window or dozing or chatting amongst themselves. Not helping me, they didn't hear what he said. "You could have got this ticket anywhere. Go on, off you get." I didn't know what to do.

Life seemed to slow, to almost stand still, then it caught up and time was real again, too real. I wanted to scream to the bus passengers, to the boys upstairs, to my Mam or McCloud or Steve Austin or the one with the big nose in "The Streets of San Francisco". But I didn't, I just got off the bus, quietly, politely even, with my rolled-up towel under one arm and my blank bus ticket in my other hand. I looked at the ticket, it had no print on it at all, I examined my thumb and forefinger. They were stained purple. Purple like a forger or a whinberry thief.

I stood on the bus stop as the bus pulled away, the people on the lower deck not even acknowledging my existence, the exhaust fumes choking the last bit of drama out of my tragedy, but no, there was more to come, an epilogue, I looked at the back window of the top deck. I could just make out the three heads of the boys on the back seat upstairs, waiting for me to pop up into the upper deck like a Tigger and accelerate down the bus towards them, instead it left me stranded. No money. No idea of how to get home.

I suddenly felt more alone than I'd ever been in my life. I was scared and saw no way forward, no way out. I had an overwhelming longing to be home, in my room, under the blankets, on the couch with my action man pyjamas and rosy glow of bath night or the friendly furnace of the "Park Ray." The brown stained plughole in the bathtub, the "Jaffa Cake" curtains in the kitchen, the chipped paint on the banister, the "maybe next year" lack of carpet on the stairs. The bus stop started filling up again for the No 67 to Glynneath. I waited for someone to approach, to take charge, to instantly take all my worries away, but nobody did, I felt invisible, unrequired, unnecessary. I moved along, to somewhere I knew, that was familiar, Victoria Park.

I sat on the bench, facing the great clock and sobbed, quietly at first, rising slowly to sporadic, rhythmic inbreaths with nasally, unforgiving out breaths. My nose thought he would join the action and released the flood gates.

35

Brain kryptonite came oozing out of both barrels, slowing only at the weir of my top lip then viscously flowing over only to be frothed up by caterwauling. As if the snout bubbles were not enough. I was in a terrible state, and I knew what was coming next: the nosebleed. I always got a nosebleed when I got upset, Mrs Rees said it was atmospheric pressure and she had a gift. As I waited for my traffic light nose to change colour, I heard a voice, a familiar voice. It used my name.

"Shwmai Lyndon, I knew it was you, duw, you look like your father. Who's your father?" "Shit it," I thought.

It was Dai Bach. The only grown-up that I knew who was of no use whatsoever, in any situation. Dai had played Welsh League football with my father and was the only person that ever mentioned him on a regular basis.

"Albert was your father, bloody good player. 'Boots on fire Jeremiah' they called him," continued Dai. I never knew my father, but I liked it when Dai mentioned him, and it cheered me a bit.

Then I remembered that Dai lived in a doorway by the Conservative Club and pissed himself twice a day and all seemed lost again. Dai was no relation to Tommy Bach who was called Bach because he was little and his dad was also called Tommy, Big Tommy. Dai was called Bach because he was enormous. "6 foot 4 in my stockinged feet", I remembered him saying. Dai never drank on a Saturday because he played football, even though he hadn't played since he found his best friend sleeping with his wife. That was twenty years ago. He never went home again. Before I could stop him, he dragged his sleeve across my face whilst gripping the top of my head, I was powerless to stop him. The mucus mass was not so much wiped away as redistributed.

Dai smelt of arse and death. "Tell Uncle Dai what's the matter, butty boy," he exhaled.

Funnily enough, he was my uncle, but most blokes I knew were. So, I told him everything, no turd un-stoned. When I'd finished, I felt better.

Ok, I'd be cwtching up with Dai next to the bins, under the painted quote from Winston Churchill tonight but I felt better. My crying headache was starting to ease, and my eyes were no longer stinging. I genuinely felt better.

Wanting to thank Dai or just to check he was still next to me I turned in his direction. What I saw startled and confused me all at once.

Dai was rocking back and forth, on the bench, his hands on his knees, his teeth clenched as he breathed in and out at double pace, his eyes were filled with a madness I had never seen in him before. Then he shouted as loud as a man who only usually mumbled could. "B-a-s-t-a-r-d." He immediately stood up and started walking in a circle with clenched fists.

"What are we going to do, Dai?" I quizzed him worriedly, hoping he had a plan to get me home that didn't involve pissing himself. "I'm not going to do anything," he announced to the world like a cowardly cousin of Spartacus. "We are going to see Uncle Selwyn." With that he pulled me effortlessly up by the shoulders, stood me straight and then nearly sat me down again when he whacked me in the chest with my towelling Swiss roll. And so off we marched, right through the middle of town. A tramp on a mission and what looked like his assistant. My hair was sticking up from the lack of combing, crusty snot to the right of my face, blood in my left nostril. But I followed. I didn't know what he had in mind.

I followed like a drum-less drummer boy, my arms beating out a rhythm that was nowhere but inside my head, in a vain attempt to keep up. "Stretcher coming through, " shouted Dai as the crowds parted in the streets of Neath, people jeering happily when they realised it was only Dai. What did he mean about Uncle Selwyn? How was he going to help?

I'd never really thought about what Uncle Selwyn did. I knew he wore smart black trousers and the shiniest shoes in the universe, but he always got on the bus to work with his jacket over his arm, covering a cap, I thought, straining my memory like a crumpled tube, squeezing out any remaining truth paste.

Too late to work it out now as Dai strode into the square outside the train station next to the old bus works. That was it. Uncle Selwyn was a station master, it all made sense now. No, my newfound conclusion was short lived, as Dai got his bearings and strode straight through the arched doorway with "United Welsh Bus Company" carved into the stonework. I watched as he wildly gesticulated to a beautiful lady with her hair up and glasses. He pointed at me outside the window then to somewhere in the opposite direction. With that he was outside again, wild eyed and glorious. "You'll be alright now Lyndon," and he turned to walk away. The lady had followed him outside.

"When are you coming back to me, Dai Bach?" called the lady. Dai stopped and said loudly. "When Swansea wins the bloody World Cup." "I didn't love him, Dai." said the lady. "I know," said Dai quietly, "But I did." Dai marched away. "Say hello to your Mam, Lyndon," then, "B-a-s-t-a-r-d." He shouted at full kilter. I knew he didn't mean my Mam. Dai stopped at the corner and looked up at the station clock. It was twenty-to-five, time for the final whistle. Dai reached into his pocket and pulled out a small, curved bottle of whiskey. It was time to drink. With that, he was gone.

The beautiful lady bent down in front of me, so we were at eye level. A spittled handkerchief was used to clean up my face whilst the task was explained with the kindest of smiles. "Come inside Lyndon, the Inspector will be out in a moment," she said. I only knew of one Inspector, Clouseau. As I waited for Peter Sellers to appear, I sat on the red velvet seat in the dark panelled waiting room, not knowing why I was there.

Had Dai Bach got me into worse trouble? Probably, because that's what he did. Causing chaos was his speciality.

I was in the waiting room for a while, long enough to partially forget the impending doom. Where was Uncle Selwyn? Did he work here? He wasn't a driver, I knew that.

The tick tock silence was broken by the slow opening of a reeded glass panelled door. It had "Inspector Jenkins" written on it, which I hadn't noticed before, and the glass gave a little rattle as the handle turned. I looked up to see a man in uniform standing before me. Resplendent in black and silver, buttons gleaming like the night sky, flawless and foreboding.

A watch chain completed the ensemble as I noticed the sword sharp creases in his trousers leading to magnificent patent black shoes. "Hang about," I thought, "I know those shoes." My eyes darted upwards to the man's face. It was Uncle Selwyn's face, under a perfectly sculptured cap with silver braiding and emblazoned with the "United Welsh" insignia. My heart began to vibrate in my chest, then started to run around, knocking into all my other organs.

It continued to space hopper about, and I thought it was only a matter of time until it burst out of my chest and made its way to Woodley's the Butcher.

I had an overwhelming desire to cry, because I was in trouble, because I was confused or because I had someone I knew that could tell me how to get home. "Lyndon," said Uncle Selwyn. I didn't answer. "Show me your ticket my boy," he said gently. I held it out in the centre of my hand. He took it and examined it carefully on both sides then took out a notebook from his pocket and slipped it inside. He then took my thumb and forefinger into his and looked at the purple ink that was just about still visible.

"Mm-hmm," came the barely audible response through his pursed, walnutted lips.

"Who was on the 57 today, Mrs Williams?" said Uncle Selwyn with unwasted words. "The new man, Len Chin, Inspector Jenkins," said the beautiful lady.

On hearing this, my day reorganised itself almost instantly. I had, in fact, been banished from Bus Land Province by evil overlord Len Chin, Emperor of Evil and slayer of the innocent. I was a huge fan of the, dubbed into English, Chinese adventure "Monkey," and this sort of rationale was something I found that I did a great deal of, increasingly so. I snapped back into the room. "He's pulling into the square now," she concluded. "Come with me, Lyndon," said Uncle Selwyn with a tone that could have served well as the last line of a war movie. With that we left the office. The beautiful lady smiled at me lovingly and added a wink for good measure. I smiled back, knowing that I would marry her one day.

I remained two steps behind him as we crossed the yard, my steps in perfect symmetry with his, hidden in his protection yet strangely excited about what was to come. Uncle Selwyn stood in the centre of the square as the remaining shoppers waited to start their journeys home. He raised his hand with the piety of a preacher, forcing the double decker to stop out of parallel to the curb. He then approached the side doors and indicated his intention to enter, the lever was pulled, and the doors opened. He stepped into the bus, and I stayed on the pavement, hiding out of view as my initial bravery got off early. "Come here, Lyndon," said Uncle Selwyn, with a softness that was out of character but intoxicating.

I joined him on the bus, my ear rubbing awkwardly against the side of his elbow through lack of space.

"Do you know this boy?" stabbed Uncle Selwyn. Len Chin opened his mouth in dubbed silence but before the subtitles appeared. "Don't speak. You will take this boy home, to Cilfrew, Maes-Y-Deri stop, before you finish your shift, and you will report to my office on Monday. Is that clear?"

Menaced Uncle Selwyn as he verbally removed his Samurai sword from Len Chin's gullet. "Yes, Inspector." said Len Chin, strangely in synchronisation with the dialogue. "Good. Sit on the back seat, Lyndon." said Uncle Selwyn pointedly. He watched as I ran up the centre of the bottom deck. I turned and sat just in time to see the remainder of a smile on Uncle Selwyn's face, out of view to the driver, then he was gone, leaving only a loud bang on the window of the bus as it pulled away. The journey home was faster than usual. Most of Wales was settling down to Saturday night TV or a trip to the pub or club or a dusky game of long lamp.

But there I was with my own bus and cuckolded driver heading home to my Mam. I looked to the front of the bus; I could see his eyes in the rear-view mirror. He didn't notice me at first and I got lost in the moment, staring deep into his soul.

I felt my power growing, like I was absorbing his earlier dominance and seeking my revenge. Even though he wasn't part of this "Phoenix from the flame" glory, I basked in the moment of the day.

How all had seemed lost, how I had single-handedly turned the tide, the table and the worm. I was Jerry to his Tom, David to his Goliath, Llanelli to his mighty All Blacks.

I had beaten you, Len Chin, overthrown your evil regime of bus eviction. I was the saviour of all nine-year-old bus peasants, protector of the weak and the inkless ticketed masses. I was Lyndon of Cilfrew.

"Shit," he looked at me in the mirror. I looked away, then back, then away and back again. This time I kept my nerve and stared at him through the safety of the reflection. "I could do this," I thought.

Spurred on by my earlier rousing imaginings, our gazes were locked, too late now, do or die, only one winner.

"Look away you bastard," I think I said quietly or didn't. He reached up and changed the angle of the mirror. Victory was mine. The rest of the journey passed in a glow of familiarity as the distance from home and a corned beef supper decreased. The pulsating love of Maes-y-Deri pulled up on the left and I walked hurriedly down the middle of the bus. The doors opened early, and he merely slowed at the stop, probably hoping I would stumble as I got off and he would get a last-minute gravelled knee revenge. I was well practised in this art, however, and hit the pavement like an Olympic gazelle. I considered my parting gift of "Cheers Drive," but erred on the side of caution. His foot hit the pedal and he accelerated away, into the sepia evening.

I crossed the road to the bus stop and waited. It was a tradition I did to all the drivers, a thank you for the journey, this however was personal. It normally took three and a half minutes for the bus to turn at the end of the village but tonight it was a record-breaking event. I heard the throaty engine approach and slipped into the shadows of the shelter only to reappear exactly as the bus thundered past. Our eyes met for the final time. I smiled, he did not.

Then silence ensued, broken only by evening song and the rattling rooks. I looked at my hands, they were now unwrinkled and inkless. I walked the short distance home, working out how I was going to explain to my Mam that I had left my towel on the bus. I looked into the kitchen window of the house next door. Auntie Betty was peeling chips for tea.

Uncle Selwyn would be home soon.

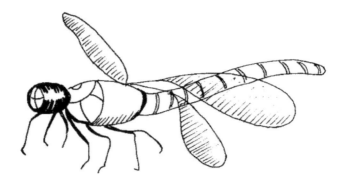

Brian the Snitch and the Wardrobe

I lay on the sun-warmed timbers of the platform, which were all that remained of the tower in the centre of Tonna Reservoir. It was the start of the lifelong summer holidays and without a thought to return, school seemed a place others went, in far-off countries, in other lifetimes, but not ours. Sun dried and as warm as a daydream, I turned over on the planks, their temporary damp chill catching me unawares. I was able to view through the missing timbers the black waters some twelve inches below. Thoughts of the battles beneath, terrifying opportunities to die in the incomprehensible depth of the darkness. I had many moments like these, without a clock measuring my life, collecting the data of my days, times when minutes and hours were never wasted but exchanged for knowledge and adventure. Lulled by the undulating waters, the endless sun and bosomed birdsong, I dozed effortlessly, in and out in a mixture of contentment and entitlement.

With meaningless seconds remaining before my self-disciplined decision to stand, climb onto the institutionally rusted railings and dive into the cold waters of the res, I took one last look into the medusan waters. I trained my eyes, controlled the focal length of my perfect, un-stigmatised child sight.
I could see the depth now, down deeper than I could before, two maybe three feet below, entranced by the secrets of the depths.

There was an air bubble, smaller than a pinhead spiralling to the surface, followed by a larger object. As it came into vision, it rotated as it rose, finding its balance before almost breaking the surface tension of the water. It seemed to be a small twig and, at first, I thought it was a windfall from the trees surrounding the waters. It bobbed and enticed like it hadn't a care in its newfound world.

Scooping it from the water, I laid it on the wood next to my head, watched as the water around it was absorbed into the dryness of the fibres of the timber. I recognised it as some kind of dead insect, resurrected from its watery tomb. I saw the power of the midday sun quickly dry the casing of the object, turning the blackness into a hazel skinned sarcophagus.

It was changing shape now, getting longer and wider as the moisture from it dissipated. Undramatically, a seam along the back of it opened and quietly, without ceremony, it got wider and longer. I could see the contents, though I could not make out any of its shape and form. There was more moisture inside the shell, and I watched as the warmth of the day continued to alter the size and length.

Then, in contrast to all that had preceded it, there was drama, minute, life changing drama, movement, inside the cocoon, which was now only the dry remnants of its former self.

I watched, transfixed as the creature expanded exponentially, breathing but not breathing. "Was it moving?" I questioned myself, "or was it vibrating gently in the breeze?" Slowly, with minuscule yet monumental effort, it lifted itself from within itself, leaving its original carcass behind. I saw a long tail unfold, uncoil perfectly to double then treble its length.

Witnessing its beginning had completely taken me away from the world. I saw the wings unglue themselves from the length of its body, fall damply alongside. The insect rested between bouts of activity, I willed it on, silently chanting my evolutionary encouragement.

The wings gently but symmetrically became perpendicular to its body. It seemed to nap between bursts as the wing expunged life from its thorax. I blew gently on the wings, this aided their formation and, spurred on, I carefully removed the remaining husk of the cocoon taking care not to remove one of its legs in the remaining stickiness of the sack.

I watched in wonder as the beautiful Dragonfly stood before me, inches from my face. Still too fragile to fly but there it was, existing, seizing life, fighting for its place in the world. I continued to blow gently along its whole length, breathing life onto it, into it.

Its wings were now strong and vibrant in blues, greens and gold, translucent in the sun. They separated and doubled in number. I watched as each leg was tested, as the tail was coiled and uncoiled in the warmth. Then, like a spitfire pilot starting the engines the wings tried to vibrate.
Start, stop, start, stop. I continued to dry it with my breath. Then fuel hit the engine and the wings burst into life, new life. It rested there for a few seconds more, then hovered millimetres above the surface of the wood, then it took off, in no rush to leave, dancing around me in what seemed like an air display of gratitude with no fear of my presence. Its circles around me got larger as I stood. Then, in a final fly by, it was off across the water, skimming and shimmering, rejoicing in life. I watched and yearned to fly away with it.

"You ok, Lynd?" shouted one of the boys. "I'm fine," I said, faltering back to reality. "What are you doing?" They persisted. "Nothing much," I said. I didn't want to tell them, this was my memory, only for me. "I'll tell my kids about this moment one day," I thought. I had never had that thought before, never imagined myself as a father. What it would be like, creating life, helping them grow, caring for them and watching them as they spread their wings and fly off into the world. I liked the thought of that, it made me smile. I paperclipped it to the memory of the Dragonfly and filed it away under the title "Nice Things." It was not the only folder in the cabinet.

We forget so many things about childhood, things that we took for granted, that we assume will always be part of our lives. The smell of the soil, its texture and sodden weight. The stickiness of ferns and the green tinge they left on your skin.

The taste of grass stems rolling around your tongue, teasing and flicking the roof of your mouth. Morning dew on your bare feet or the warm raindrops of a sun shower.

I found the perfect apple once, on a tree in the scrublands we called "Pethrams."
It was low to the ground and the branch had grown inside a bramble bush. It had been missed by every other dirty nailed scrumper and remained, unbothered, in its shady cove. I had marvelled at its perfection.
It was almost entirely red, and I had studied its symmetry. Its connection to the branch was strong and unhindered, a single leaf sprouted at its base and the blackberries that surrounded it seemed to look on in protective adoration. It had reached its unlikely potential; it had not had to suffer the indignation of the wind and the fury of the rain. I had sat and watched it that day without a thought to harvest or to bite into its perfect skin. I dreamt of it that night and in my unladen dream, I was the apple, undiscovered and waiting for the glorious adventures of the world to begin. I had returned the next morning with my sketch book and HB pencil, eager to capture the last moments of the Pippen Prince before his Coronation. The apple lay on the ground, a single leaf keeping vigil. Rabbits had feasted on its flesh and council workers, made up of black ants and woodlice hurried to clean up the murder scene. The apple spurned my pity, and I realised I had been taken in by the vanity of the saga, my own vanity. The apple had completed its task admirably, with distinction. Like all the other windfalls it was destined to simply form a link in the chain, and it was honoured to do so. There was no requirement to be mentioned in dispatches or to pin a medal to its breast. It was just a bloody apple. Maybe I was the apple after all.

Being a kid was dangerous. We never knew it, why would we? We were too busy enjoying ourselves whilst arrows of death whistled unnoticed past our heads and bear traps of disaster were unconsciously avoided by mere inches.

For the sweet love of Elvis, if I ever thought that my kids had so carelessly gambled with the flame of their candles in the way that I had then I would be writing this tale from the armchair in the sunny window of "The Home for the Parentally Insane."

We had jumped from trees forty feet above the river, the water being invisible to us as we left the branch, only to be revealed when we broke the cover of its leaves, avoiding the rocks with our coin toss naivety of death.

We lay next to the railway tracks on camping nights, inches from the wheels of the coal trucks as they hammered by. The noise that remained in our heads throbbed us to sleep with an innocence that our Mams would have gladly slapped out of us.

There was one event that refuses to politely wrap itself in nostalgia and rest comfortably in my filing cabinet of childhood. It visits me occasionally and we sit in awkward silence in the parlour of my dreams. The original cast members have been replaced with my kids or loved ones I am responsible for or those of whom I love with every beat of my heart. I write of it only to release myself of its burden, which I have carried for far too long...

We didn't have gardens that required hose pipes or push along mowers, there were no lawns or borders with happy flowers or orchestral vegetables in musical rows, preparing for a harvest symphony. In musical terms, our garden was pure punk rock. Anarchy ruled. With sofas and broken dreams, brambles and fractured promises. There was a history that lay beneath. The story of a lost childhood made of old prams and airless footballs, trikes and missing in Action Men.

There were no Arran sweatered role models to breathlessly tease in kickabout heaven in our gardens. No barbequed Sunday afternoons with the charcoaled sweet smell of roasted beasts. The highlight of our year was usually in late August when the rain had doffed its cap to the sun and the wind had stripped the garden of its moisture.

The washing season had begun, and the piously judged bed sheets had been released to a fluttering freedom, though they were removed with haste when they heard my mother play her Shirley Bassey long player on her turntable that she had placed next to the open window of the kitchen. This was an early warning system, of sorts, like the medieval mountain beacons that had come before. Ange was having her fire.

Once a year we set our garden alight. It was usually late afternoon, and it took about three hours to complete. There were no complaints, just the shutting of windows and the gathering along our tinned sheet boundaries of friends and neighbours who enjoyed the opportunity to gossip the smoke into submission. The desired result was the napalmed neatness of the biggest garden in the street. Half a bowl of water was kept at my Mam's side in case of emergencies. Health and Safety was paramount to her as she squirted the paraffin from an old Fairy Liquid bottle across the front lined brambles and commenced the fire-slaughter with a casual flick of her lit cigarette.

My Mam was pretty, bloody cool.

The Bull Ring Gang were there, Bryn the Frock, Will in a Minute, Tommy Bach and Me. It had become an annual event to rival penny for the guy or bonfire night, a chance to flirt with danger in full view of what was regarded then as parental supervision. The only warnings that were ever issued, however, were more concerned with personal belongings than personal safety.

Comments like, "Watch you don't bloody melt your new wellies," or "Don't pull a thread on that new jumper, you'll not have another one," were commonplace. All the wellies and jumpers were far from new and had been part of the village for longer than we had.

They had been circulated around the Mams when their offspring had grown too big, to the next in line who had kids the right size.

This guilty secret was never spoken of, there was no embarrassment between the previous owners and the current. The only time there had been a breaking of this unspoken rule was when Catwg Primary rugby team had played Bryncoch in a cup match and, more because of my endless determination and freakishly accurate over arm throwing skills rather than my size and athletic prowess, I was playing hooker, in the middle of the front row of the scrum.

As we crouched to engage, facing our old enemy, my counterpart from Bryncoch looked at my feet and exclaimed, quite innocently, I now realise with the benefit of hindsight. "Those are my old rugby boots; my Mam gave them to the Jumble sale last week."

The whole of the opposing pack had burst into laughter. My embarrassment was hidden as the two packs collided and thankfully my tears fell straight to the muddy turf without staining my cheeks. Bryn, however, had a different emotion running through his veins.

Playing prop forward on my right-hand side and linked in embrace with his left arm to me. I could feel his anger rising as the scrum lurched sideways with his lack of self-control. I saw his fist clench and the moment the referee was on the other side of the scrum, he landed three perfectly timed punches onto the nose of the "Super-grass" who was helplessly bound to his props with both arms. The scrum disbanded immediately leaving my nemesis standing alone with blood streaming from his misshapen nose. "I think he must have caught a knee, Mr Davies," said Tommy, playing scrum half, as the rest of the team obscured the guilty party, as we had always been taught to do. "The ball hit him in the face Mr Davies, I saw it all," shouted Will from the side-lines, wearing Mr Davies' oversized coat. As Mr Davies Catwg led the squealing piglet over to Mr Davies Bryncoch he looked at me and winked. We loved Mr Davies Catwg.

Back at what looked like a scene from "The Wicker man," the fire was in full blaze, the flames taking the ash from twigs and leaves on a spiralling journey to the sky. "Lyndon," shouted my Mam, "Mrs Rees has a wardrobe she wants to burn, you and the boys go and fetch it round." It was like a starting pistol had gone off. In seconds, four small boys from Wales were sprinting up the road towards Mrs Rees's house whose garden backed onto ours. In under a minute, we stood in front of the wardrobe in awe of its splendour. The wardrobe was enormous, in the darkest of woods, ornate and foreboding. It had a central, single door and hanging space to the sides. It had no drawer at the bottom like my Mam's Mam's wardrobe and stood upon stunted, lion-headed, ball and claw feet with scrolled detailing and reeded panels on both sides.

At the very top of the cornice, as we looked heavenwards, like cherubs gazing on the Ark of the Covenant for the very first time, Mr Rees (Deceased) had fixed a framed cross-stitched plaque. It read "Thou be to God."

We were all in agreement. "We can't burn this," said Bryn. "We could use it up the den," speculated Will. "It would make a bloody great tree house," said I. We looked at Tommy Bach, who was always the ideas man in such situations. He stood in silence, his mind putting in an extra shift, his hand on his chin. "This, boys," we waited with bated breath, "is a submarine."

We all fell silent, pondering the possibilities of Tommy's statement. It was a pivotal moment, the start of our greatest adventure. "Are we in?" whispered Tommy with his trademark dramatic inflection in his voice. We simultaneously burst into euphoria, dancing around in ecstatic embrace.

We were invincible, heroes all, we were the Bull Ring Gang. "You bloody taking it or what?" interrupted Mrs Rees, her hair in curlers and breathing deeply through a newly lit "Superking." Her pencilled eyebrows were trying desperately to escape.

We promised a tutting Mrs Rees to return in the morning to take the wardrobe away and headed back to the remnants of the blaze. The sweet smell of sausages cooking on an open fire met us with a beautiful assault on our taste buds.

We sighed in instant disappointment to find there would be no porky bangers today but on the bright side the pyromaniacal ensemble had located, too late, the body of Mr Prothero's aged black Labrador, Trev, who had gone missing a week earlier and had received a send-off fit for a Viking Lord.

It was early next morning that we arrived at Mrs Rees's to pick up our submarine. There was no sign of life at no 12. Bert y Biniau, the brother of Mr Rees (Deceased) always stayed over on a Friday to keep Mrs Rees company, which we all agreed was very nice of him.

We manoeuvred the wardrobe by shuffling and rocking it on its sturdy feet but only after placing a bag of tools Tommy had gathered from his Gramp's workshop inside and locking the door with the key that was still in the lock. The wardrobe was remarkably light for its size, and we easily lowered it, pivoting on its back legs so that each of us had a corner to carry. Will and Bryn at the front and, due to our lack of statue, Tommy and Me at the back. Each of us had our towels and trunks rolled up and used as padding on our shoulders to make the mile and half journey less arduous. It was all downhill to the river and we knew that this underwater apparatus was never coming back up the hill.

After only a couple of hundred yards, we stopped to chat to Cecil Dykes, known to us all as Cess, local legend, and dispatcher of Rooks. Folklore had it that he could shoot a worm from a beak from a half mile away, though my Mam had said this was because he usually missed. The self-proclaimed King of the Welshmen, Cess had the best one-liners in the world, and he had delighted us for years with his sometimes cruel but gut clenching stories. In a parallel universe, he could have been a Sicilian hitman or a hired gun in the Wild West.

He had the look of a ruthless killer and the heart of a missionary Nun. He loved us kids and we loved him. We couldn't wait to see what he had to say today with the spectacle that was laid before him.

"What you got there, boys?" said Cess, warming up his repertoire. "It's a submarine, Cess," exclaimed Will, proudly. "Duw, handsome that is. I used to be a Captain of a submarine, boys, in the War, but I couldn't handle the pressure," smiled Cess, he was off and running. We all laughed but only me and Tommy got the joke. "You need to paint it yellow, boys, I've got some Council paint in the shed. It should get you all the way to Liverpool." "That would be brilliant Cess," squealed Tommy, his mind shifting up a gear. "Well, come and get it now Tom Bach and you can have your Gramps bloody shovel back too," said Cess, walking off towards his house.

"He died last spring, Cess," said Tommy, sadly.

"Well, I know that mun, he was my best friend, but I can still hear the old bastard going on about it, come on," stabbed Cess gently. We all laughed at the swear word which had been delivered with the skill of a marksman and the huge dollop of affection that engulfed it. They both walked away, Cess had his arm around Tommy's shoulders, and they were deep in conversation.

While we waited for Tommy's return, we laid the wardrobe on its back at the side of the road and pretended Will had been killed by it falling on his head, to see if any of the infrequent passing cars stopped to help. Nobody did.
Tommy Bach returned in minutes with a large pot of paint with yellow tears and an old brush.
"Where is the shovel?" I asked. "He couldn't find it," laughed Tommy. Off we went again.
Down the pub hill, down the long steps, sliding the wardrobe on the central handrail.

The river was now in sight, but the trees ahead muffled the sound. As we passed New Road, the last bastion of civilization before we would be completely feral, we saw Brian Brain in his garden.

Brian was the bespectacled incarnate of evil. He was as skinny as a pencil and his thinning hair was always buttered to his head. He always wore a shirt and a tie with a knitted waistcoat in which he kept a foldaway pair of opera glasses for surveillance. We were terrified of him as small children but as he was so universally despised by all the village, he had become a source of ridicule to us and was the only adult in our world we would dare give cheek to.

I had made up a story whilst camping with the gang that the "Child-catcher" from "Chitty, Chitty, Bang, Bang" had gone on holiday to "Oz" and had a bunk up with "The Wicked Witch of the West." Brian was the resulting lovechild, destined to incarcerate the children of Cilfrew and spoil their adventures with his flying monkeys. As I picture him now, his skin has a light green hue.

"What you got there, boys?" said Brian. The boys looked at me. It was usually me that started the ruse, then they would join in. "Mrs Rees passed away in the night Brian, it's open house up there, you'd better be quick," I relayed in a serious tone.

"Bloody genius," whispered Bryn. "What's left?" said Brian with some urgency. "Her Mam's China, the TV and her collection of silver spoons," enticed Tommy.

"Anything else? Is there a crowd?" enquired Brian, desperation in his voice as he hurriedly slipped on his jacket and fumbled into his pockets for his bicycle clips. "We were the first there Bri, if you're quick you might get her Rolls Royce or her speedboat," quipped Will. This was the wardrobe that broke the camel's back. We all burst into laughter, dropping our burden heavily to the floor, grabbing our knees in stooped hilarity.

"You bloody liars. You vicious little swines. I'll get you for this. I'll tell your parents. I'll contact the Council. I'll…, I'll phone the police," snarled Brian, his fists clenched at his side, his John Lennon glasses to the fab fore of his nose. With this flurry of threats, he rushed off to the "Twatphone" to call Commissioner "Flash" Gordon at the Neath and Gotham Talbot Police. The rest of the journey to the river was a pure joy. It was interspersed with spontaneous re-enactments of the scene with Brian. Impressions of his voice, fictional dialogue of his conversation with the police and best of all the thought of him knocking Mrs Rees's door to be met by a bewildered Bert-y-Biniau in his underpants and socks.

The river now roared with laughter at our side, eagerly anticipating the adventures afoot. We had reached our destination, Devil's Pool.

Devil's Pool had been, for the kids of our village, a no-go zone. It was dark and deep and the rocks that cradled it were black and slimy, wet from the constant spit of the plunge pool. No sun ever got through due to the thick feathery plumage of the overhanging trees and the angry mood of the place was enough to terrify the bravest of summer swimmers.

There was a rumour and therefore true, that a family of four had come off the road and crashed through the dry-stone wall at the top of the bank and the car was at the bottom of the pool, some fifteen feet below with the bodies still in there, safety belts still fastened, with no satisfaction that they had reached their final destination.

I hadn't helped the situation by telling a story around the campfire that every night the Devil swam up from below to take a shit and eat badgers.

But that was before Tommy took charge. He had arranged, on our previous visit, to take on the Devil himself.

Armed with his Grandad's saws, hatchets, machetes, and his trusted disciples we climbed the trees around Devil's Pool and, under Tommy's instruction, removed many of the overhanging branches that deprived the pool of the sunlight it craved. The more foliage we removed, the more sun hit the rocks and the water of the pool.

Within hours what had been hell on earth had been transformed into a tropical paradise. We brushed the rocks of the leaves, we cut back bushes to form diving platforms and we cut down the sign with skull and crossbones on it that said "Beware - Deep Water." We had put it with our collection of other signs that included, "No Trespassing," "Danger 40,000 Volts" and "This Bridge is Unsafe - Risk of Death." We would use them somehow, in the future, but that adventure had yet to be written. We now gazed upon the most beautiful sight we had ever seen, the pool had flourished in the sun, the treacherous laverbread rocks were now covered in the snooker velvet softness of the day. What was once hell, was now heaven as it bathed it in glorious God shine. We put the wardrobe down and circled it like Apaches with sciatica, stretching and bending and making unnatural guttural sounds as we tried to shake off the monumental effort of its steerage.

"What's next Tom Bach?" I said, knowing the answer. This was Tommy's moment to shine. "You lot need to sod off for a bit and let me create. Go on, give me an hour." We knew not to argue and had no intention to do so.

Tommy was a temperamental genius when it came to inventions, he saw things that we could never see, made things that we never realised needed to be made. He was however one of the most stubborn and bloody-minded creators that there had ever been and was always two minutes away from smashing up his creations or stropping off in soft muttering madness if we ever challenged any of his ideas or, God forbid, disagreed with him.

"Ok Tom, but be quick, yeah, I can't wait for this," cajoled Bryn. Will and I shot glances at Bryn but Tommy was already lost in his calculations to care. We left him to it as he retrieved the bulging bag of bits from inside the wardrobe, speaking gently to himself, the world around him fading away as ideas were birthed, and escapades took their first breath.

We spent the time productively, fixing a swing from the great oak tree that hung over the pool, resplendent in its new haircut.

We nailed three planks of wood to the trunk to make it easier to climb to the diving branch in old, wet daps and piled the old branches that we had cut down the week before across the width of the river where the water rested in the aftermath of Devil's Pool and crawled, exhausted, over the shingle before continuing its pilgrimage to the River Neath. This provided us with an exclusivity from the outside world, delaying the discovery of others that this was, indeed, heaven on earth.

We patiently dived and swam and sunbathed. Will and I felt the need to distract Bryn, who was the most impatient of us all with questions we knew he couldn't resist. "So, Bryn, would you rather have the legs of an ostrich or a kangaroo?" said Will. "Easy one," delighted Bryn. "Kangaroo every time. I could jump the school fence at dinner time, hop to Tonna chippy for rissole and chips and hop back to clear the gates before the bell." "An ostrich could run it quicker, you could have a "Sherbet Fountain" from the post office too, if you got a sweat on," I teased. Will nodded in mock agreement.

"Then how am I going to get over the fence, boys?" snapped back Bryn. "Ostriches can't fly, you dickheads. You need to think these things through." Then he paused. "It could save your life one day." And there it was, Bryn's catchphrase. The one we set the trap for and was snared so very easily. "Good point Bryn," we laughed in unison. Bryn never knew. Forty-five years later he still doesn't know but still he falls into that love trap more often than not. There was a loud, shrill whistle.

Only one of us could whistle that well. We looked up on the bank next to the river; it was Tommy.

In his trunks with an underwater face mask on and something written on his bare chest in mud.

It took a while to work it out but then we realised it was the Superman symbol but drawn in reverse. I suppose, nowadays, Tommy would have been diagnosed with dyslexia but back in the day we just thought he hated reading and writing and avoided it at all costs. He put one foot on a rock, put his hands to heaven and shouted, "Your carriage awaits."

Because his nose was inside the tightly fitting face mask it sounded very much like he had been deaf since birth. We scrambled up the bank, desperate to see the fruits of his labour and disappointment was not on the agenda.

The three of us gasped in amazement at what was before us. Perched on three rocks and a stump was the greatest submarine we had ever seen, even though, obviously, this was our first. It gleamed in luminous yellow in the sun, enhanced by the canvass of bluebells that surrounded it and it helped to highlight the random buttercups that were interspersed in the sea of blue.

It seemed even bigger now and on the top of it was the large domed door of a washing machine. The feet had been sawn off and lay to the side. It had, fixed with baler twine to a long stick, the hose of an old hoover running its full length of about six feet, the other end was looped up into the submarine. It had an old plastic drainpipe at the front with an elbow at the top kept in place with plastic brackets. In black letters down the side was handwritten the words ``The Yellow Sub."

I noticed in the mud beside the craft three attempts to spell the word submarine, none of which were very close. The last one was indecipherable as it had an angry boot print through the middle of it.

"Thou be to God" was now screwed to the front like a celestial cigarette sponsor on a Formula One racing car. We stood in awe, unable to speak. It was magnificent. Better than anything Troy Tempest, Captain Nemo or Jacques Cousteau had ever captained, and it was ours. "It has a viewing panel, a breathing pipe and a periscope," announced Tommy, "though the periscope doesn't work since the mirrors didn't fit in the pipe. I've got ballast inside and I've sealed the joints with roofing bitumen before I painted it."

"It's fantastic, Tom," congratulated Bryn, ruffling his hair. "A work of art that, Tobermory," admired Will, using his personal nickname for him, courtesy of the handyman from the Wombles. "It's your best work yet Tom Bach, well done," I marvelled, grabbing him around the shoulders and giving him a shake. Tom stood there proudly; his face mask clouded with emotion. "We have to christen it before we launch it," announced Tommy, removing his mask, a red oval framing his face. "We need some champagne," said Will, having never seen a bottle in real life, only on the telly. "I've got a better idea," said Tommy, pulling down the front of his trunks and pissing on the back of the submarine. We all laughed and joined in, christening all four sides, the steam of success rising in celebration.

"She'll be unsinkable now," said Bryn, showing his inexperience as a submariner. We all laughed along, trying not to let him know we were laughing at him. Then he realised what he had said and laughed too, making the collective joy spiral into near hysteria.

We got the sub down to the shore, it seemed heavier now with the rocks inside as ballast and the paraphernalia attached, even though the door had been removed. We rested for a moment, then lifted the submarine above our heads and manoeuvred ourselves awkwardly so that we all stood inside the body of the submarine, supporting the weight on both sides.

Bryn was at the front, behind him was Will, then Tommy then Me. "It's dark in here," echoed Will. Already the outside world had disappeared without a trace.

The whole space illuminated as Tommy switched on a small battery-operated lantern and hung it on a nail on the ceiling of the space. "Whoa, that's better," we all agreed. "You've thought of everything, Tom," added Bryn. However, we were moments away from finding out he hadn't.

The thrill of excitement filled that capsule. We looked down at our feet and edged towards the water, stumbling gently on the unsure surface of the rounded pebbles. Further in we went until the water was to our waists. Will sang "In an Octopus's Garden," as we carefully rested the sub on the surface of the water. The relief was great as the weight of the craft was taken by its initial buoyancy and we had more freedom to move about.

It was only then I realised Tommy had fixed our collection of signs to the inside walls of the submarine.
"Nice touch Tom Bach," I nodded in full agreement with the others. "Check out the breathing apparatus," glowed Tommy, as he slipped on his Gramp's old gas mask with the end of the breathing tube fixed to it. "Amazing. Outstanding," contributed Will and Bryn.

The sub was now starting to gently sink under the weight of the ballast so forward we walked, down the soft incline into the deeper water. We edged it forward but held none of its weight. We could see the level of the water silhouetted on the sides of the sub as we went deeper.
The water surface was now level with the top of the sub, and we were officially under water. "It works," we all cried in celebration. "Let's go deeper," dared Will with no opposition. So, we did. It became colder, darker and the air thicker.

Our voices became more condensed as we went lower into the depths.

"My ears just popped," delighted Tommy. "And mine," confirmed Bryn, excitedly. The water was now rising inside the sub.

"Don't worry, it's the pressure," reassured Tommy, taking the ballast stones off the side and releasing them to the riverbed. The sub became a little more buoyant and the water levelled off, but only momentarily. We were now maybe four feet under the surface of the water, and it had started to rise again. "I don't like this Tommy," I said, the first to question the mission.

The water was now halfway up the level of the inside of the sub and had formed an air pocket of about eight inches high. "Don't panic," said Will, looking at Tommy for reassurance.

"It's fine, isn't it, Tom?" pleaded Bryn. We all looked at Tommy. He looked frightened. "Abandon sub," shouted Tommy. Right at that moment the weight of the water above the sub forced it to the bottom of the river, trapping us all inside. The air pocket was now only six inches high and getting smaller. "What do we do, Tom Bach?" I pleaded. Tommy was deep in thought.

"Bryn, you and Will are the strongest, you must lift the sub whilst we swim out to the surface, get some air and then we will come back down and lift it for you two to escape." instructed Tommy. "You won't come back." Bryn started to cry. So did Will. "You'll leave us to die," he cried. "No time to argue, let's do it," I said aggressively. With that, Bryn and Will snapped into action.

Taking a deep breath each, they went under the surface and after an elongated, few seconds, the sub started to slowly move off the bottom.

"Go," shouted Tommy to me, as the light of the lantern went out as the water lapped against its base. I didn't need telling twice. We both took a last breath inside the lost sub and went under.

There was no visibility at all, and we had to feel our way to the bottom. There was a small gap between the bottom and the sub. Tommy went through easily and I followed, scraping my torso on the slimy rocks beneath, then we both panicked to the surface. It took an eternity to find air, we had been deeper than we thought. The noise of the river was deafening as we filled our lungs. In out in out. The freshness of the air had never tasted so good; we had quickly acclimated to the warm, thick air in the sub.

The temptation to swim to shore and run for help was overbearing but we knew it would mean the sure death of our friends. I wanted to cry.

I looked round to see Tommy diving again below the surface, I followed but first filling my lungs, I hoped, not for the last time. Reaching the bottom of the river was quick but at first, I couldn't get my bearings and find the sub, then my shoulder brushed against a sharp corner and there it was. I planted my feet against the bottom and lifted. The wardrobe was already two inches off the bottom with Tommy's solo effort, working together it was soon about eight. I felt one body swim past my leg then almost immediately a second. They were out. We had done it.

I swam for the surface and was the first to break back into the torrents of the plunge pool, followed desperately by Will, gasping, crying, screaming, laughing, filling his chest with life. Then Tommy's head appeared beside us. He was the best swimmer of us all and could hold his breath the longest.

"Bryn's leg is stuck," panicked Tommy, "It's trapped under the wardrobe." With that Will was gone, under the surface. Bryn was his best friend. We both followed immediately. At the bottom we found Bryn, though he was giving very little effort to escape the wardrobe. Tommy and I repeated our lift, but it was heavier now with no air left inside. A squeeze on my arm meant, I hoped, I prayed, that Bryn was free. We all seemed to break to the surface together.

Bryn showed no signs of life as we dragged him through the shallows to the shingle beach of the river. Bryn's lifeless body lay on its back on the pebbles in the sun.

Will sat on his chest shouting for his life, pleading for him to be alive, slapping his face to try to wake him.

We didn't know what to do, we paced and cried and pleaded for Bryn to be alive.

Then it seemed that we were attacked, thrown to the ground, pushed violently out of the way.

The attacker was huge and dressed in black, it was all so confusing. Something landed at my feet, it was a Policeman's helmet, I picked it up, it was getting wet. "Out of the way, stand back," it was Mr Chapman, the local bobby. "Why was he there?" I thought to myself, it made no sense.

We all stood back a couple of feet and Mr Chapman turned Bryn over before first checking his airway. He held Bryn in one hand and with the other hand gave him a thunderous slap on the back, waited a few seconds whilst rubbing his back, then again. No sign of life. He looked around the faces of the three of us. He had no expression, but I thought I saw a tear in his eye, maybe it was a splash from the river. He gave another attempt to slap life into Bryn. Softer this time but with more precision. Seconds were minutes then a cough, a splutter, river water spurted out of Bryn. Mr Chapman still held Bryn and gently rubbed the rest of the water out of him.

Then, carefully, he rested him on his hands and knees as Bryn vomited for victory. Will joined in in support. Will had a very high gag reflex. I watched as Mr Chapman took himself away, gazed down the curving path of the river, lost in its inevitable path to the sea. With his back to me, he took a handkerchief from his notebook pocket and wiped his brow then his eyes. He took a deep breath and turned to face us and spoke. "Let's get you boys home." He then turned to me, "I'll take that, Lyndon." I had never, in my life, felt prouder that someone knew my name, even to this day.

We gathered our things, wrapped them in our towels then walked home with Mr Chapman. We were subdued at first. I said, "I'm dying to get home." Bryn, with a wit that was quite uncharacteristic said quietly, "I've done enough dying today." Even Mr Chapman had to raise a smile at that one. We reached the beginning of New Road. Predictably Brian Brain was in his garden having spotted us with his spy glasses a half mile since. He stood there with his hands folded in triumphant revenge as it seemed we had been arrested for the malicious kidnapping of a wardrobe. As we passed the house, Mr Chapman stopped us. "It's Mr Brain you must thank for making it through today boys, without his quick thinking it would have been a very sad day indeed. I would say a very heartfelt thank you if I were you." said Mr Chapman. "Thank you, Brian," we chorused unenthusiastically. Brian Brain's life peaked at that very moment in time, and he would spend the rest of his life regaling the fact that he had saved our lives. We never disagreed with his account. We owed him that, at least. At the top of the pub hill, we parted company with Mr Chapman. "Thank you, Sir," we all said in unrehearsed unison. "Straight home now boys and remember to think things through a little more." Then he paused. "It will save your life one day." Bryn looked on with an open mouth as his hero and ours walked away, continuing his beat, keeping the people of Cilfrew safe. "Dave," said Cess. "Cess," said Mr Chapman, as they passed in greeting. "How did it go, boys?" said Cess. "We nearly died in a Yellow Submarine," explained Will. "I hate that bloody song," said Cess, not taking our claims seriously. "I've found that shovel Tom Bach, come by tomorrow to pick it up." "Ok, Cess," said Tommy. Cess walked away whistling the tune to "Yellow Submarine." We stood there, watching him leave.

For Four Small Boys from Wales, the words to that song would never, ever, be the same again.

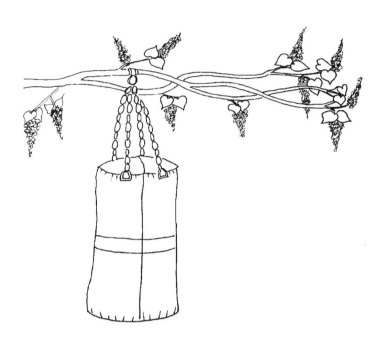

He Could Have Been a Contender

The boy was never lonely. He had never been alone. All his life he had been surrounded by friends who he loved and who loved him. His position in his gang was of a trusted leader who spent much of his time making sure they were included and protected from others that would do them harm in their mild and gentle childhood. There were no predators in their world, just the occasional reprimand of adults and older siblings, hellbent on spoiling their fun. He was kind and happy and he was known by all that knew him for his unbroken smile and for being an expert navigator between the crystal-clear springs of boyhood and the muddied waters of grown-ups. He had been raised by women who were strong and powerful who had cajoled and cuddled him into submission in a blanket warm, world of love. The hierarchy in his sphere was clear and concise. Mam, Mam's Mam, Aunties, older cousins, and babysitters. All female, all kind and all tasked with forming an upbringing, a village, a community and preserving the status quo. There were smacks, telling offs and early nights when protocol was, not so, innocently broken but the aftermath was short and instantly forgiven. His life was simple and easy, and his worries were restricted to being home on time, keeping his bike in working order and not embarrassing his Mam in the weekly Eisteddfod of Sunday School.

The sun shone and rain-soaked days were spent below the embrace of swaying boughs, the twisted timbers of barns and the under-used resource of concrete bus shelters. Men, in his world, were kind and encouraging and he frequently felt the glow of their acknowledgement. A ruffle of the hair, a wink or his name used in greeting was the limit of his involvement in their seemingly uncomplicated lives. Like all addictions, however, it was unnoticed at first, but the boy had started to realise that his craving for their attention was starting to gather momentum. He had never missed having a father.

It had never really crossed his mind. It was impossible to miss something that he had never known. Of course, he had had moments of fleeting jealousy when his friend's fathers had fetched them from a nightly game of football at the rec, when the failing floodlights of the day had forced the fixture to be postponed, only to reconvene in the morning. His teammates had been flung onto cowboy shoulders or rode piggyback on a giddy up stallion, whilst he plodded alongside on Shank's pony.

The ogre with the emerald eyes also stood at his side on the day that his best friend had been given his first bike. It was not the bike that was the centre of his longing. The twist grip gears, the off-road tyres or the suspension saddle. Beyond his grasp as these seemed to be, it was the way his pal's father taught him how to ride the bike that caused the pit of his stomach to ache so strangely. Their hands on the seat and handlebars, keeping them in a straight line. The running alongside, the constant encouragement, the genuine delight as his little man won the day. The boy had run home, took Neil Llewelyn's old bike from behind the shed, it had been there a while.

He wheeled it to the top of the incline by the bus stop, jumped on, readjusted the pedals, and freewheeled the hundred yards to his front gate, slamming on the brakes, which skidded to a stop due to lack of recent use. Exhilarating though it was, there was no excited crowd, no shoulder grabbing congratulations and nobody else to remember the moment.

The boy had occasionally borrowed fathers, from others, on a short-term loan. Dickie Manning had taken him fishing a few times, a man who oozed kindness from every pore of his leathered face. Built like a bull, Dickie could have smiled for Wales whilst effortlessly ripping the heads off any passing Viking invaders, placing them on spikes next to his beloved aviary and farming the maggots for the chaffinches. He was huge and small both at once.

His face carried the scars of a decade long rugby match where you suspected he had inflicted more pain than he had received. Dickie had never lost the ability to be a child and the boy, in his presence, could swear and piss outside without any parental scolding. Dickie and the boy were friends. He had taken the time to teach the boy to fish, given him a rod, shown him where to dig worms, how to mercilessly thread them on the hook, laughed like a bear when an eel wrapped itself around the boy's arm as he danced the polka and squealed like a seagull on the tow path of the canal.

Dickie and Vicky had recently started a family and their firstborn son was called Richard, after his dad.

This had set the precedent of all their children having names that started with the letter "R", which, only noticed by the boy, it seemed, was the only letter of the alphabet that Vicky had not, completely, got to grips with. In years to come, hearing his beautiful, flame haired neighbour summon her flock from her front step pulpit, tea towel in hand, would form another part of the washing line on which the boy's childhood had been pegged out to dry in the endless summer warmth of his life. Dickie and the boy spent less time together as he and Vicky tried tirelessly to produce their own First XV, but their friendship was to last a lifetime.

Shoes became tighter and bicycle seats were elevated. The boy's world expanded by a few square miles as his adventures got bigger, always with the safety net of a warm bath, a bedtime supper fry-up of leftovers, his books, and his dreams.

He remembered, vaguely, the day that Michael Regan entered his life. It wasn't a pivotal moment, or it hadn't seemed so. Regan made his Mam happy. She smiled more, laughed more, did silly things that she had never done before. The boy liked that. There was no clapping of thunder after a lightning strike, no earth-shaking awakening.

He was just there, then he was there some more and eventually he never left. Regan was kind to the boy and spoke to him when his mother was around. He asked him about school, rugby, football and their shared love of greyhounds. When his mother left the room, the conversation stopped. The boy had put it down to the man's shyness which he felt was an attractive quality to possess.

The boy loved greyhounds. He walked and hunted rabbits with Ted Jones's old dog Jeb. He spent hours in the woods and along the old tram road. Jeb was slow and docile and seemed to reflect, like old men that the boy knew, on a life that had gone unnoticed. Then, Jeb's ears would prick up, the moment would be electric. The boy's hand would be on the clasp at the end of the lead, always ready. The rabbit would break cover, the clasp released. Jeb would throw off his retirement, his long evenings by the fire and explode with every pent-up sinew of his machine toned body in pursuit of the kill. The thrill was unrivalled, the kills were rare, unless you counted myxomatosis season when murder was effortless, but the boy's nightly dreams grew darker. He was told it was humane, he believed it even. The jury of his nightmares reached a different verdict. He knew every inch of Jeb's physique. His hindquarters which were long, muscular, and powerful, his hocks, delicate and efficient. His well sprung chest with the gentle undulation of his rib cage. The forelegs set well into the shoulder, perpendicular to his long, narrow head. He was the epitome of strength and power yet used it so passively when not in the throes of competition.

Strangely, the boy saw the same qualities in Regan.

Regan was a boxer, a good one. He had boxed for Wales and the house became a shrine to his achievements. The pictures of him in his crimson, three feathered tunic and gold figured boxing trophies adorned every spare wall space and empty shelf.

He worked hard as a roofer every day and trained without mercy every night. He ran and skipped and hit the bag hanging from the boy's lilac tree in the garden every evening.

This in addition to the mythical stories of the early morning and weekend sessions in the boxing gym. The boy sat and watched for hours, in silence. Sometimes from his bedroom window, sometimes from his lilac enthused vantage point.

He saw Regan's physique change the closer he got to a fight. He saw him grow leaner, faster, and stronger. The repetitions were bigger and the resistance to the pain grew less. The boy was engrossed in his journey, became invested in his success. Silently and without ceremony, the boy developed a new and uncharted emotion: admiration. The boy started to hear stories of his legend. Of how Regan was the last boxer to beat Colin Jones, who would go on to be British, European and World Welterweight Champion after a rematch with legendary American fighter Milton McGory.

The boy heard that Regan had been refused his professional licence because of a childhood injury when his twin brother had thrown a dart at him and punctured his iris, resulting in a blind spot on his left-hand side which had fallen below the stringent requirements of The British Boxing Board of Control. This fact alone was to be a burden for him that was harder to carry than the six lengths of four by two the boy had witnessed him carry effortlessly up a two-story ladder. The boy had met Regan's twin brother, David, a few times. Though facially similar, it had seemed to him that Regan had sucked the very life energy from his womb-sharing sibling, leaving him the gaunt shadowy weakling that visited the house on a few occasions, making no positive contribution whatsoever. Regan, however, seemed to have the strength and resilience of two men, foetus infused, rampaging through his fights, dispersing gum shields and reputations like they were apple blossoms.

Prior to bouts, there were huge meals of steak and mashed potatoes, pasta, and protein of any kind. Closer to the big night, there were early morning pints of raw eggs, washed down with red top milk from the bottle. The boy sat up late into fight nights, waiting for the delayed scorecard or the imaginary waving of the referee's arms on another emphatic knockout victory. He never went downstairs, he never joined the celebrations, he just listened to the muffled voice of the returning gladiator, sitting silently on the landing for any snippets of the night's event. He slept more soundly with every triumph.

One night, however, the victories stopped. They didn't taper or become irregular, they just stopped. There were no losses. There were just no more fights. Regan had become the biggest fish in a pond he had long grown out of. Having beaten everyone in the division, defended his Welsh title on numerous occasions and without an invitation to the professional ranks he had nowhere to go, there was no one left to fight. Without a bout to prepare for, without an opponent to hate and destroy and consume his anger and his rage, and focus his mind and body, he was lost. Gone was his routine, his discipline and drive. He went out into the world looking for a final, career-defining, fight and he found one. It was to be the biggest fight of his life and one he was never equipped to win. The rematches were daily, and the beatings were costly. The trophies were not worth winning and made of fool's gold, tarnished with self-loathing.

The towels were soaked in beer, not sweat. He had found an opponent: the booze. He found someone to hate: himself.

The boy watched on in silence. Sometimes from his bedroom window, sometimes from the lilac tree. He saw Regan struggle with training, it was like watching the preparation for a fight in reverse. The repetitions became less as the resistance to the pain diminished.

Still addicted to the routine but slowly weaning himself off the only life he knew. His gym became a pub, any pub.

Alf, his loyal trainer and manager had tried to help and succeeded, for a while, persuading Regan to train a new set of up-and-coming youngsters at the gym. The boy, on one occasion, had felt a huge weight of embarrassment to be caught hitting the "lilac" bag in the garden by Regan one day.

He had looked at the boy with no emotion showing on his face, then turned and went into the house without a word. The drinking continued, but to his credit, Regan never missed a day at work, though this seemed to be more to fund his new pastime rather than to keep his new-born son, the boy's baby brother, safe and warm.

Alf turned up one Saturday morning, in late August. The glorious vibrancy of the school holidays rang out like a church bell. He was in an old "Commer" minibus. It was faded red with piggy eyes and a gentle smile. Alf sat in the driving seat with his trademarked Woodbine in the corner of his mouth and the toilet-rolled first aid of his weekly shave. With his salt and pepper hair slicked back with a comb that was missing as many teeth as the man himself. He was a joy to behold. After a short but animated conversation with Regan, Alf beckoned the boy to round up his pals.

Today was Boxing Day.

In minutes, the bus was filled with half a dozen excited boys in vests, shorts, and daps. The boy's mother was tasked, unnecessarily, with explaining to their mams their otherwise unnoticed absence for the day. Their journey was filled with over-seat sideswipes and wrestling as the pecking order of the day was decided and self-proclaimed champions were crowned before a single punch had been thrown. The boy sat in silence behind Regan who, for the entire journey, nodded and agreed with Alf's opinions on the world.

The gym was in the small village of Croeserw, in a valley outside Port Talbot which the boy had imagined was on a par with other such boxing venue greats as The Albert Hall and Madison Square Garden. The reality was very different indeed. The boxing gym was built on the extremities of a set of allotments on the side of a brackened, rock-stained hillside. It was no more than a collection of other buildings sewn together with tinned sheets and tarpaulins. The entrance was an old pair of chapel doors with "In God we Trust" carved into the arched frame. Someone had written over the word "God" with the word "Alf" in white paint. As the boys chattered and punched their way up the packing crate steps, the boy held back, taking in the moment of the ramshackle gym and the beautiful severity of the landscape on both sides of the valley, undulating down gently to the smoking, industrial dragon's mouth of Port Talbot.

Inside the gym was a site that the boy had not expected. Like a tardy Tardis, the place was deceptively big. He was met with the all-consuming smell, that he had grown to know from Regan's boxing kit that dominated the washing basket on a near daily basis. It was sweat and liniment and muscle rub.

It was leather and blood and disinfectant all clenched together to form a knockout punch. There was a rhythm in the room that called you forward, like a gladiatorial orchestra warming up for a concert of pain. The sound of the huge punch bag thudding into submission, the speed bag bumpity, bumpity bumping along, acting as the metronome of the scene. There was the spring quartet of the four posted ring, bouncing to the tune of the canvas as the head-guarded ballerinas pirouetted against the sweat soaked ropes. There was the nasal assault of the punches thrown and the gum shielded exhale of the punches received. The gym smelt of men, of fathers and imaginary older brothers with legendary grandfathers looking on and conducting the ensemble.

To the boy, it was a pugilistic jumble sale of all the dreams he had never known he had ever wished for. After a twenty-minute warm up of sit ups and press ups and running on the spot, overseen by a barking but encouraging Alf, the heavy breathing gang of boys took to the ring... but not before being gloved up with the largest, softest gloves in the gym. The boys were put in three pairs and shown how to move and guard and jab.

The boy thrived in the blanket of guidance, of nurture and instruction. There were wild punches from some of his pals, understandable excesses of frustration from years of tolerating school yard bullies and bad fathering. The boy, however, moved about the ring, used the ropes to turn defence into measured attack, tucked up when the punches rained down and jabbed his way out of difficulty.

The months of watching Regan from his bedroom window had paid off, how he moved and balanced his body, his footwork and how he swung his upper body from side to side to escape confrontation. The session had finished, and the boy felt good, like he had achieved. The boy had found something that he enjoyed, had some ability at. Most importantly the encouragement from Alf had flicked a switch in his head. The boy wanted more, more Alf, more warm words, more boxing in his life. Alf led the boys off into the changing room to be degloved.

"Stay here, boy," said Regan, placing his hand solidly on his shoulder. The boy had forgotten he was there. He hoped that there were more words of encouragement coming his way, he wanted Regan to tell him he had done well, that he had learned from him or beyond his wildest dreams, to be told he was proud of him.

He didn't.

As the boy stood in the ring alone Regan stepped on the bottom rope and held up the middle one. Into the ring stepped another boy. He was taller than the boy, more muscular and he moved his head side to side as he bumped his colourful, smaller gloves together. He proudly wore the colours of the boxing club and his matching shorts contrasted stylishly against the white laced up boxing boots. His "Lonsdale" head guard seemed to mould effortlessly into his face, this together with his gum shield destroyed any means of making out any of his features. "Just do a couple of rounds, see what you are made of," said Regan.

The boy was unsure as to which of them this had been addressed. The boy's opponent was strong looking, older by at least two, maybe three, years. The boy wasn't frightened, but a feeling of dread started to creep over him as the noise of the gym seemed to lessen as the boxers took an interest and gathered around the outside of the ring.

"Fight," said Regan, casually, like it didn't matter. It mattered to the boy, whose heart had started to race almost uncontrollably under his white, oversized P.E. vest.

The boy stood firm, placing his feet well to steady himself for the gentle sparring he had learned some minutes before. His adversary advanced and started to move his upper body back and forth.

The boy felt the jabs from his opponent hit the top of his guard, they were heavier, thrown from the shoulder and not from the side as with his friends. The boy tucked up and kept his elbows in.

The older boy backed off. The boy moved forward, threw some punches of his own. They seemed ineffective and weak, his gloves were soft and oversized. The boy chastised himself and tried to punch harder but again they had no effect.

Another barrage of gloves hit the boy's head guard, this time catching his nose and upper lip, unprotected by a gumshield and any real boxing prowess. The boy's overwhelming feeling was of embarrassment, he was glad his friends were not there, relieved Alf was not witnessing his performance. The boy tried to jab, to move forward but his opponent easily avoided the undisciplined punches, the ones that did land seemed to, again, have no effect.

The stronger boy seemed to drop his gloves, turn to the corner, and ask for permission. Then the boy saw it, permission granted. Something broke inside the boy. As he stood there in his black plimsolls, grey school socks and Neil Llewelyn's old football shorts, he saw Regan nod to the older boy; he saw the betrayal of a love that he had no right to believe ever existed. Regan looked at the boy. It was the same look that he had seen when he caught him hitting the bag under the lilac tree.

Suddenly he felt so alone, wanted to get out of there, wanted Alf, wanted his Mam. The punches came quick and fast, disorientating him more with every blow. The boy's guard, his only defence, disintegrated with every blow. He turned away, trying to find the solace of the ropes but they deceived him as did the corner post. His only hope was the canvas who embraced him like a long-lost friend. His fight was done, the pain stopped. The boy was holding on to the bottom rope, trying to focus from the blows. He saw himself in the full-length mirror on the wall behind the back of the ring, he recognised his smallness and his ineffectiveness. He tried to hide his embarrassment but in the mirror was another opponent who he had hidden from all his life. The boy couldn't hold it in anymore. The tears came, quiet tears of loneliness in a room full of people. He did not want to turn round, to face Regan who he imagined was laughing and hugging the other boy.

"What the hell are you doing Mike?" shouted Alf, returning from the changing room.

He climbed into the ring and punched Regan square in the chest, a blow that would have felled a normal man. Alf helped the boy from the ring, the tears continued but this time it was for the kindness shown and not the crushing embarrassment. All admiration for Regan remained in the corner of the ring in the bucket full of spit and snot.

The boy and Alf knew why Regan had done it. They knew he hated his life, his missed opportunities. They realised the childhood he had had. They knew his father beat him the most out of his five sons because they were the same. They knew he struggled in conversations, that he was intimidated by anyone who spoke in full sentences and words of three syllables. Alf excused it. The boy never did...

This story and many others continued for seven more years. The tales were familiar and have been penned by many before. They were long and sad and there were no winners, only losers. The boy faded away and was eventually replaced by a man who met a woman and had a life full of his own triumphs and disasters.

He was still kind and caring but always had the steely and silent, yet seldom used, resource of his upbringing. The man believed there were two types of good fathers. Those that had had good fathers themselves and those that hadn't. Each was a journey that could result in the right destination. The man had chosen the right path.

It was forty-five years later that the man found himself back in the town that had formed him. The town that had educated him, celebrated him, and taken his virginity, which was handed over early and without complaint.

He had, that weekend, reminisced and enjoyed the company of old friends that remained and lamented, in glorious inebriation, those that were not. He was done, his visit complete.

With time on his hands before the last train out of Neath he ventured into a pub from his youth where his mind had revisited many times over the previous four decades, reliving his times of glory, when life was a one-way, hand-made, staircase to success. Gone were the silver dancefloors and strobing adventures of the 1980's, the pulsating throng of the sons and daughters of the Miners' Strike. In its place were the remnants and battle weariness of the soldiers left behind. The man recognised many faces there, smiled in silent appreciation as he placed some loose puzzle pieces of his past. It was now a pub for the overspill of the town, the unrequired and unloved souls of that glorious, dirty, little town. At the bar he scanned the faces again, using the database of his life to try and photofit any remaining convicts of his past. He found that the less he concentrated on this the more success he had. A walk, a mannerism or a turn of phrase would mechanically select a memory and out of the machine of his mind would pop a little card with the answer on it. Tiring of the game and aware of his reducing time of departure he saw, through the window, at waist height, a very small man's head moving parallel with the windowsill along the front of the pub through the etched glass of the pub's name in reverse.

It amused the man as it appeared to be a floating dwarf. Smiling into his beer, he watched as the diffused image got out of what he assumed to be a Motability scooter, unfolded a walking stick, and entered the pub.

Regan walked through the door. Unmistakably and unremarkably, it was Regan. The man froze in time. Years fell away. The smell of stale beer suddenly became the overbearing aroma of the pub. He was old, broken, fragile and so very small. His flawless Paul Newman looks had been hidden beneath years of nothingness. His Macintosh was grubby, his thinning hair was uncombed and, judging by his stick-man-ship, he was not in the best of health.

Still the man watched, unable to turn away. Regan was but two feet away as he ambled down the two steps next to the door.

"Alright, Son," he said to the man. The man laughed, it was involuntary, he couldn't control it. The absolute, kick in the balls, irony of the situation was bordering on the comedic. The man knew he hadn't recognised him, he knew it was just a greeting drenched in the local dialect that he had both issued and received many times that fading weekend. The old man sat in what was clearly his usual seat and carefully removed the loose change from a lady's purse which he kept in the pocket of his Mac. A kindly barmaid brought a pint to his table with the greeting, "Hello Michael, how are you, my darling?" "Thank you love, I'm good," was his response. The man stood at the bar, entranced. He noticed the heaviness of his own pint glass, the shakiness as he tried to casually lift it to his lips. He tried to look around the rest of the pub to continue his meaningless game, but it was now a charade as his gaze was magnetically brought back to Regan. The man succumbed to the past, he passively pedalled towards the memories he had spent so many years trying to forget.

He remembered his Mam's tears, the shouts and screams in the dead of the night, the pinches and punches, the backhanders, the teasing, and taunting and worse, the ignorance and denial of his existence. In his nose or in his mind were the familiar smells of the gym and the pub became filled with the noises of a dozen men fighting for a future. The man knew himself very well. He knew this was not somewhere he needed to be and that he had the ability to walk away and package memories, to store them and use them in the future when there would be times when his strength was to be tested most.

He finished his pint as a scruffy young man entered the pub. He was too young to be part of the man's now forgotten game and he paid him no further attention.

He did, however, notice how several people turned slightly away or raised their racing papers just a little higher upon seeing the track-suited no mark.

The man put the strap of his bag over his left shoulder and his jacket over his right arm. He was more than ready to "get the hell out of Dodge." He glanced one more time over to Regan who had been joined by another man, equally unimportant and dishevelled. As he turned for the door, he heard the loud, weasely voice of the younger man which neither improved nor deteriorated his first opinion of him.

"Hey, it's Old Bill the Boxer. How are you, Bill? Still getting the rounds in I see. Come, old boxer, do a few rounds with me." The man stopped between the bar and the door. He looked over to the young man, he was dancing around in front of Regan, bobbing, and moving, throwing air jabs in his direction, annoyingly close to Regan's face who unflinchingly looked away.

"My name is Mike," said Regan quietly. "His name is Michael Regan and he beat Colin Jones, now Fuck Off," said Regan's cornerman. The man paused, "not my problem," he thought, lying to himself. He continued to the doorway.

"Colin Jones? Who, the Fuck, is Colin Jones?" said the younger man, "Come on Boxer Bill, show us some moves, come on, get up, I'll buy you a pint if you can catch me with a punch, come on." He kept on goading as the man turned around. He saw Regan sat in his seat, looking away from the greasy, mulleted younger man. Regan's movements were slow and ratchetted as he turned to face his opponent. The man saw something he had never seen in Regan's face before but recognised it from deep inside himself: fear.

The bell sounded for the last round.

The man put down his coat and bag at the bar. He walked over to the table where the two men were sitting. "I'm sorry, gentlemen, I couldn't help overhearing your conversation," said the man.

"I wanted to put this young man straight on a few things." He placed his hand gently around the young man's shoulder, he shrugged it off immediately. "Who the Fuck are you?" snarled the ugly little scrote. "That is not important," said the man.

He aggressively grabbed the younger man by the back of the neck and by his right wrist. He shook him violently and pointed his face towards Regan. The young man struggled but he was out of his depth and submitted almost instantly. The man explained quietly without a trace of menace in his voice.

"This is Michael Regan; he was Welsh Welterweight Champion for four years consecutively without loss. He was also Welsh Champion at two other weights. His record was forty-two wins, three draws and two losses that were very early in his career. In his prime, he would have beaten ten little shit-stains like you before breakfast with one hand behind his back whilst reading The Racing Post. You are not fit to lace his boxing boots, empty his slops bucket or be in his almighty presence. The next time you see him, you will not speak to him, if he speaks to you, you will address him as Mr Regan. Is that clear?" The man squeezed his neck tighter and gave him a light throttle. Regan could not take his eyes off the man. "Y-y-yesss. very clear," said the younger man. "Good boy," said the man, "now apologise." "I'm s-sorry," the young man spluttered. "NOT TO ME," barked the man, shaking the young man's neck violently.

"I'm very sorry, M-m-mister Regan," he panicked, looking straight at Regan, who ignored him completely whilst still staring at the man with the narrowed eyes of some unfathomed recognition.

"Now, off you go young man and next time know your place in the world," said the man calmly, releasing his grip on the younger man who darted for the door.

As he left, he turned and shouted," I'm coming back for you, you cunt." and left. The cornerman stood and touched the man's arm. "Thank you, son, I'm Pete." The man smiled and said, nodding to them both. "Pete, Mike, it was nice to see you both, I must be going, I've got a train to catch." He walked over to the bar and repeated his leaving preparations. He took one more look at Regan, it was to be his last. He turned to leave and saw three figures lurking outside the pub, behind the frosted glass. His concentration, however, was still on the two old men.

"Who was that, Mike?" said Pete the cornerman.

"That was my boy," said Regan.

The man closed his eyes momentarily and thought sadly to himself.

"I wasn't his boy. He wasn't my dad. But there had been a time when he could have been a contender."

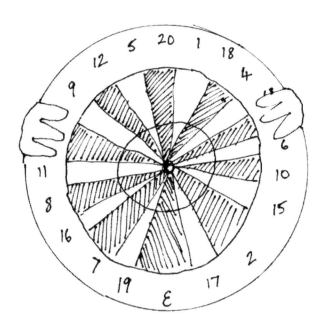

Windy Hill Farm

The afternoon had departed without my consent.

It was dusk. The dissipating glory of the finest of days. The crimped, crinolines of the powdered clouds softly surrendered to the soot of the evening. Rooks drunkenly made their way home, angry at the shortness of their visit. Winds shushed the trees to sleep and all around the farmyard shadows curved and lingered, fingering the corners of the broken buildings, pointing the way to the inevitable darkness. An exhausted sun had long since called it a day, nodding passively to a rested moon who proudly assumed its role as the evening's guardian. It hung low and blurred, silently sharpening its edges in preparation for the contrasting black sack of the night. A cat lay in wait as the overworked mice panicked their way back to straw woven homes in watering cans and hole peppered buckets. Owls adjudicated the contest and a dog tapered gently, unaware of the hunt. The twisted, rusting detail of the day softened in shape and form to create ebonised canvasses on which to paint the landscape of the night.

I knew every detail of Windy Hill Farm. It had been my salvation, my bolt hole, my sanctuary from the smallness of my life. I had breathed its air, shared its secrets, and contributed minutely to its history. I had spent every moment of my weekends and school less days in her embrace, quietly lamenting, in unimportant sadness, that she would never truly be mine.

Jim and I had built a fortress of straw. Not to keep the world out, but to keep ours within. It was inside the old barn. Made of bales, stacked in a pyramid, with one entrance and no exit. We had inexhaustible materials and unlimited labour. It had taken hours to construct and would normally have resulted in a violent dressing down by Jim's dad, for wasting time, for not finishing his jobs around the farm or daring to fashion a childhood. But that was before.

We were in no danger of it happening now. Dai would not care that we had spent the day building the perfect den, where we could sleep and play and hide from the world, talk about girls and efficient ways to seek revenge on fathers or stepfathers or Hitler or Gwilym the Prick. Dai didn't care about much these days except the pub and the bottle under the sink. Not since Jim's mam had died.

I never knew why she died, I never asked. I suppose, looking back, I should have but these were times when that wasn't done. When things were not discussed or counselled or dealt with head on. Problems were ignored, stored inwardly and another normal was raised from the ashes of the silent fire. I saw no difference in Jim. The fear of his dad, the constant criticism and back handers was instantly replaced by the complete devastation of losing his mam. He seemed the same, I'm sure he wasn't, but it seemed that way. The only small consolation of losing his world was that he was now ignored by the person he most despised. His hatred for his dad was never self-centred, not decided upon by his treatment at his hands, but by the way Dai treated his mam. Jim only deviated from the script once in my company. "I wish he had died instead of her." Simple and concise and the summation of the start of a difficult life.

Jim was not without love, he had it in abundance. It was for one thing, one person, one diamond in his bucket of pig-shit. Jim's sister was six months old when her mam passed, Jim was twelve. She was his life and life force.

Charlotte was well cared for and happy, she giggled and laughed, and all these things were because of Jim. He did everything for her like it was second nature to him.

He was his mam, not his dad. He looked like his mam. Dark and strong, soft and determined. In Dai's eyes, he was her.

Whether it was the devastation of losing Mary or the guilt that he felt for the way he had treated her when she was still here or maybe his heart was black as tar and always had been, but he could not bear to look at, or be around his children. In recent months, the farm had fallen into disrepair, unnoticeable to the untrained eye, and he had started to go to the pub earlier and stay later.

That night, however, was going to be perfect. Jim had bathed the baby and fed her and put her to bed. She usually slept through the night, most nights. Her bedroom was on the top floor, above Jim's and the house was always as quiet as a tomb. The Egyptian silence was broken only by the Grand Pharoah clock on the middle floor, gently reminding the current keepers of the vault of the dynasties that had reigned before. It stood there like a vertical sarcophagus, demanding the attention of the silence. He had left her window open so that we could hear if she woke up, which she seldom did after her creamy, straight from the cow, feed at bedtime.

We sat in the yard, waiting for Dai to return, it should be about midnight but tonight was a Friday and so we sat in the back of the hay trailer and without watches, watched the sky watchers, watch us in return. It was an easy silence, broken only by wishes and fantasies and adventures that we believed, in that moment, could come true, that would transport us off to lives that we did not deserve with people we would never meet but our imaginings were always as disappointing as cold tea within moments, but still we dared to dream.

"My mam says that everyone that goes to heaven looks down through a hole in the night sky and watches over us," I offered clumsily. "That's why we have stars. The light is heaven behind the holes. When they look through, it makes them twinkle."
"That's a pile of horse shit," said Jim.

"Sounds like your mam has been on the Woodpecker again, like last Christmas when he gave me a puff on her fag." "I remember," I said, a little embarrassed of her shoddy parenting but mostly relieved that my mother's deranged theories on the universe had not been too highly scrutinised.

"Well, my mam is not in heaven, she is in Tabor graveyard with a slab of granite on her head. If she were up there, she would let me know," hissed Jim. A comet shot across the night sky, emblazoned in a golden tail, arcing, and illuminating the darkness for the briefest of moments. I sat up, I could not find the words but turned to Jim with the widest of eyes and my mouth open, expecting him to do the same. Jim was no longer looking at the sky, his gaze was towards the end of the long, uneven drive that leads up to the farm. "Dai is back," he drawled without emotion. I looked to the skies once more. Mary was gone.

Dai morse coded his way up the twisting road, hitting every pothole with the front wheels of his Land Rover. Right, right, left, right, left, left... a sequence that he had subconsciously memorised to keep him from careering down the steep bank, even under the darkest or most inebriated conditions. We stood in the doorway of the barn, in the shadows, out of sight. The Land Rover lurched into the yard looking for trouble but every object it had picked a fight with on previous nights had been forewarned. It vomited to a standstill and Dai got out slowly but only after first checking the cobbled farmyard was still to be trusted. Leaving the Land Rover door open and the lights still on he stumbled to the house, kicking imaginary cats, or the landlord's last order bell as he went. When he was in the house, we saw the stair lights go on, counted every drunken step silently in our heads until it went off, only to have it replaced by Dai's bedroom light moments later.

This was only long enough to see if the bed had moved significantly since the night before, then it went out a second later before Dai collapsed onto it to complete another day. When this, all too familiar, sequence was complete, Jim went over to the Land Rover, turned the lights off, removed the ignition keys, put them in the side pocket and closed the ill-fitting door. We then had what seemed to be a minute's silence. Both of us standing in the farmyard, looking at the huge farmhouse as if to acknowledge its power, its part in both our lives. My escape and Jim's prison. I always felt the house had two lives, two souls. The summer sweetness of the front, with its unkempt, rose crested windows that smiled a welcome to all visitors, always contrasted dramatically with the rear.

The back of the house was almost constantly in shade and was a last dumping ground for life's debris that was deposited around the yard in Dai's hurry to be fed. It was trapped in its own chaos, lost in the never-ending immediateness of carrying on, regardless.

"She will be fine now," said Jim, breaking the silence and revealing our thoughts had not been aligned. "We will check her in a bit." This was the part of the weekend we had both been looking forward to. Free to just be kids, free to just talk and laugh and forget the farm and Jim's responsibilities. I had this trick, I used it to snap Jim into the moment, to draw a line under his day. It annoyed him, but he liked it too. I rushed him and got his head under my arm and rubbed my fist against his head, then released him immediately, taunting him to seek revenge. It worked, I could hear his playful anger as I ran for the den, confident I could get there before the attack happened. I was just inside before I felt him grab my leg, firmly and with great purchase. There was a split second, then I felt myself being dragged with some force, falling the six soft feet of hay until I hit the floor of the barn. I looked up to see Jim's rear end disappear into the single bale entrance, laughing uncontrollably. Mission complete. I joined him inside.

There were our two sleeping levels with blankets and pillows from the house. There were bottles of pop and apples from the orchard, harvested the previous summer. There were copies of The Beano and football magazines and a dartboard with five darts, all in complete darkness apart from the light from a single match as Jim carefully lit the old paraffin lamp held on the prongs of an upturned pitchfork whose handle had been forced between the bales on the far wall. We were home.

"What shall we do first?" I said excitedly. "Darts," said Jim. Jim liked darts, but our game of darts had a boyhood twist on the original game. It was nothing to do with numbers or tallying up or double tops or bullseyes. Our victory was a different one. Our game had a name, it was called "Russian Darts" after "Russian Roulette," made up on the spot after watching "The Deer Hunter," one unforgettable evening. The game was basically for one person to hold the board with their eight fingers arranged enticingly around the perimeter of the board. The object of the game was simple, to hit the fingers of your opponent with a dart. You were free to move your fingers around the board but never to let go. That would result in a free dart which would be poked into an area of your body of your opponent's choosing.

We were both equally inept at this game. I tried to avoid Jim's fingers but always seemed to hit him. He, in turn, was desperate to hit mine but never had. "You hold the board first; I'm going to get you this time." Jim's fingers were big and thick, like a man's, with hard skin with layers of healed over blisters, his nails were thick and dirty and on the few occasions I had mistakenly hit flesh with the ancient, blunt darts it had not even drawn blood, it had just embedded in the leathery skin around his nails. My fingers were small and soft and pink and clean, and it had become Jim's sole ambition in life to skewer me to the board.

His aim was as bad as ever, missing every time with the first three darts.

Then he missed the board completely with the fourth, the dart, burying itself, between my legs, in the hay, narrowly missing my leg.

I laughed nervously and looked at Jim for a similar response. His face was focussed, his eyes narrowed, and I suddenly realised this was the moment he would get his revenge.

Statistically I was buggered, he had missed too many times, this was it. I stopped moving my hands around the board, closed my eyes and accepted my fate. I knew that Jim, a creature of habit, moved the dart three times forward and back before releasing it. I counted, in my head, one, two, three. This was it, my hands gripped the board, my fingertips went white... I waited and waited. The anticipation was unbearable.

"Did you hear that?" said Jim. I opened my eyes. Jim was still holding the dart, but had his head cocked to one side, like a loyal sheepdog. "It's Charlotte," panicked Jim, stabbing the last dart into the bale next to him and heading for the exit of the den. Headfirst, he was gone. I took a moment to let the relief wash over me and secretly promised myself that I would never play that game again. A second later, I blew out the flame of the lamp and in the assaulting blackness dived for the small, now invisible, hole in the hay. Within seconds I was standing next to him in the farmyard, lit only by the head bobbing moon, whose cloudy entourage encouraged him to sleep on the job.

I could hear Charlotte crying now. The open window to her room was providing the only soundtrack to the night, apart from the apple orchard choir, lovingly lulling their love of the night. Hers were not restless stirrings or temporary rest stops between dreams; they were solid, heartfelt tears of which the undeniable need to comfort was overbearing.

Jim stood there unflinchingly, gathering every piece of information, before embarking on his task. Making sure the mission was carried out with the utmost efficiency.

He didn't like the house at night, Jim hated the dark. Not outside, outside he was fearless. In the house, however, he had to have every light on. Mary had been the same and this had caused much friction between farmer and wife, resulting in Dai fitting a coin metre to the fuse board. The house had been converted from town gas to mains electricity in the fifties and the outdated wiring had meant a constant threat of short circuiting and the resulting darkness that followed.

Jim, battle ready, headed towards the house. "I'll come with you Jim," I said instinctively. "Do what you want," snapped Jim, then "Thanks," in a glanced apology. We entered through the large back door of the farmhouse which was down an awkward set of dog legged steps. The first light switch was ten feet away and in support and succumbing to the mounting melodrama of the moment I found myself holding onto the sleeve of Jim's jersey. Instead of rebuking this act, I felt, in the moment, Jim took some comfort in it.

The mood instantly changed as Jim pressed the toggle on the brown, Bakelite light switch, long since painted over but wear had, once again, revealed its original colour. The downstairs hallway was bathed in light as our eyes adjusted. Our pace quickened now, with our path clearly lit. We ran in unison, still linked by Jim's sleeve, and quickly we were on the first floor of the house. Charlotte's cries added an ever-increasing urgency to the moment.

As we placed our feet on the first tread of the slightly narrowed staircase to the second floor the house was, once again, plunged into darkness with a deadening thud from the meter. "Fucking coin slot," snarled Jim, "Why did he ever do that to her?" I felt no requirement to speak.

Charlotte's cries suddenly became more intense, more urgent, she seemed upset and frightened. We should have run but we didn't, we couldn't. Jim pulled away from my grasp and backed up onto the landing. I hadn't noticed the sound of the large clock up till then, but here it was, hammering home the drama of the darkness.

I heard the door of the clock open, and Jim removed something from inside. I just stood, nailed to the second step up to the next level of the house. I felt him next to me again but resisted his woolly comfort blanket. As we continued up the stairs to the upper landing the moonlight finally flooded the upper level, released from the cloak of the overhanging landing, flowing down the stairs. Still the endless, breathless torment of Charlotte's tears continued. I saw immediately what Jim had removed from the belly of the clock.

It was a shotgun, his grandfather's shotgun. It was huge and double-barrelled. It was ornate and elegant and terrifying to me. "Why have you got that Jim?" I over-whispered unnecessarily, which seemed demanded by the moment. "Sshh," said Jim, silencing me immediately. Braved by his arsenal and nature's floodlighting we picked up the pace to the top landing, the excruciating cries of the baby getting louder, the closer we got.

Tick tock clicking clock.

Charlotte was now hysterical, I had never heard her cry like that before, discomfort and sadness had now been replaced by something else. They had been replaced by fear.

Click clock ticking tock.

Finding ourselves outside her room, we stopped. The door was ajar, shards of light escaping through the gap with the door frame. The lunar light was always strongest through Charlotte's window.

As Jim pushed the door open with the barrel of the shotgun my participation in the evening ended. Limited though it had been since we left the barn, I had played a minor part. From that point on I became nothing more than a bloodied bystander, a voyeur of the violence of the next few moments. Neither of us had any required dialogue, the page was empty, but what was about to take place was to change us both, for the rest of our lives.

Charlotte's cot was against the wall, highlighted by the glow of the moon. She was animated, arms flailing, trying to escape her invisible tormentor, our eyes adjusted once more. There was something on her chest. I thought, at first, it was a soft toy, a teddy bear, or her brown bunny she was never without. Then it moved, violently moved, scritching and scratching. The cries of the baby were deafening now. Jim moved past me into the room, raising the gun as he cautiously chose every step. Then a floorboard betrayed him. He stopped. Then we knew. We knew the face of our greatest fear.

Old Dic, Jim's Granddad had forewarned us of this moment.

We thought it was "The stuff of nonsense," a tale to frighten two gullible schoolboys round the yard fire to the smell of his pipe. But here it was, as real as a punch to the face.

The creature looked up at Jim. Its eyes were black, soulless, and evil. The fur around its mouth was matted in black blood. Instantly, I pieced the terrible scene together. Blood was dripping from a series of bite marks on Charlotte's lip, the blood mixed with the creamy milk she had regurgitated in her sleep. Milk that had awakened the bloodlust in the huge grey rat that sat astride her torso.

"There's a Grandfather Rat on this farm, boys, and one day you will have to kill it, before it kills you." Old Dic's words were now taking on a chilling new credibility.

"Don't you corner him. If you do, be prepared to end it there and then. If you don't, he will find you. He'd be twenty years old now and angry as a chained-up dog, cruel as the devil himself."

The rat was the size of a terrier, and his fur was grey from age, his tail, ringed and scarred, doubled its length. Then came a noise from hell itself, screaming from every bloodstained, razored tooth in its furious mouth. It leaped out of the cot, getting purchase off the quilt folded over the rails. Claws outstretched, teeth bared, towards Jim. He stood deathly still; the gun raised to his shoulder. The shotgun exploded, illuminating the room in an almost beautiful violence, the noise instantly plugging my ears from any further destruction. The Grandfather Rat hit the floor, some eight feet away, thrown backwards by the force of the blast. Blood splattered the whitewashed wall.

It was writhing and screaming, in what sounded like anger, not pain.

The shot had removed one of his back legs, but still it moved along the floor, gnashing and scratching towards Jim, leaving a trail of blood in its wake, its claws desperately trying to grip the wooden floor for another attack. Jim did not move away, as I did. He never flinched or had thoughts for his mam and his warm bed. Jim turned the shotgun around and using the butt of the gun and two hands crushed the skull of the rat with blow after blow, each one harder than the previous one. It refused to die, but eventually Jim ended him.

"Die, you bastard," said Jim calmly as the Grandfather Rat stubbornly obliged.

Jim handed me the gun and picked up Charlotte. She instantly buried her face in his neck, desperate for her horrendous ordeal to be over. Her crying calmed, subsided quickly to a low hum, interrupted only by heart-breaking sobs.

I put my hand on his shoulder, trying to think of a suitable line to say. Before I could come up with something original there was a sudden crashing open of a door on the lower floor. "What's happening?" slurred Dai, "Where's the gun?" Followed instantly by the sound of a drunken man falling down a flight of wooden stairs, unmistakable as it was unexpected.

The two of us looked over the upper floor banister rail to see Dai unconscious on the lower half landing. A small silence, then Jim gently passed the sleeping Charlotte to me, her head resting, exhausted, on my shoulder, the wound on her lip thankfully had stopped bleeding.

The lights came on the lower level of the house. It hadn't been the meter after all, just a short circuit from the bad wiring. Jim, almost unconcerned, walked towards the top of the flight of stairs down. With a quiet nonchalance, he took the gun. Instantly, I thought, to return it to the clock. As I watched him descend the stairs, he did not stop at the clock and continued down the stairs, to the lifeless Dai. With the shotgun in one hand, held at the balance point at the start of the barrels. Upon reaching his father, Jim used the end of the barrel and poked him with it, not gently, more of a prod to move along a stubborn heifer. Dai adjusted slightly and moaned drunkenly. Then Jim began to cry, like he was letting go. Letting go about tonight, letting go about his mam and letting go of any feelings that might have remained for his father. As he cried, it got louder and more desperate, they were the tears of a lifetime, never cried before and with a silent, solemn self-promise, never to be cried again. At their crescendo, Jim rested the end of the gun against his father's chest.

"Dai, you bastard," he screamed, spit spraying uncontrollably from his mouth.

"No, Jim don't do it, please," I shouted, remembering the unused cartridge in the shotgun.

"Please, Jim." I waited, closed my eyes, turned Charlotte away from the staircase, relinquishing any control I may have had in that desperate situation. There was nothing I could have done. The gun went off.

"Nooooooo," I screamed. Then it went off again and then a third time. "That can't be," I thought, opening my eyes to see the gun resting against the wall on the stairs.

The gun went off for the last time, but it wasn't the gun, it was the huge brass knocker on the front door. I listened as Jim's neighbours, the Powells, were let in, shouting in panic of what they had imagined the scene to be. They had been convinced, from the gunshot, that Dai had killed himself.

Local gossip had put him as odds on favourite, with his recent behaviour in the pub. Nobody had tried to prevent this happening, but the weavers of yarn had continued to knit a good story. With the police sirens screaming their arrival, I handed Charlotte to Mrs Powell and quietly sneaked out of the back door. I walked the two miles home, the streetlights highlighting the blood on my shirt and splattered on my neck and trousers, the blood on my collar was from Charlotte's lip, the rest was entirely rat. I told my night-dressed mother that I had had a nosebleed. It had seemed the cheapest ticket to slumberland.

Tomorrow would reveal the truth, although I was unsure exactly what that night had truly revealed.

Epilogue - Windy Hill Farm

Gone were the potholes, the twisted, rusty fenced reminders of the foreboding entrance to the farm. The sharp incline was now protected by mature laurel trees seducing you up the manicured drive.

Summer flowers softened the hard edges of the borders, and the crunch of the gravel gave my hiraeth an unwelcome announcement to my nervous approach to the house.

I had not returned to Windy Hill Farm since that night, twenty-four years before. That night had ended so many things. My love for the farm, my need to escape and it was the last time I slept through the night for the next six months, tortured by the images, the flashbacks, and the possible alternative endings. My friendship with Jim had changed irreversibly overnight. It never ended, but our friendship was now a burden of secrets that neither of us could carry alone but could never share, especially with each other. The change in Jim was dramatic. He forcibly removed the shackles of childhood, like taking off a harness that chafed into his overloaded shoulders. He altered physically and seemed older than his years. Within months he was both man and boy with a gait that was broad, strong and assured. His voice became deep and different.

He had from that night taken over the farm in all but name, dropping out of school and making all the decisions. It was said that, from that night, he had released many late-night beatings upon his father who had aged at an even faster rate, fuelled by the drink and the lack of care for himself and others. Dai had died three years later, found face down on the drive, drowned in a pothole that had seen him home so safely on so many occasions, after a farewell drink at the pub. One of many.

I was at Dai's funeral. So was Jim.

But only when he drove past the graveyard on his old Massey Ferguson, eyes forward, crunching the gears on Tabor Hill with cow-shit on the trailer.

With the help of the Powells, Jim had eventually secured full guardianship of Charlotte who had grown, it was said, into the image of her mother, filling everyone's lives with joy that knew her. She carried Jim's happiness for him, waiting for the day that he could accept it back. On this, his wedding day, he was to take his first downpayment.

Rounding the corner onto the refurbished cobblestones, I audibly expressed my shock at the transformation of the farmhouse from the last time I had shared its beauty. It was a true Cinderella moment. Her dirty face, back then, had stifled her beauty, but now, it was shining through for all to see. The roof and windows were new, and the dark Welsh stone had been re-pointed, painstakingly, by a true artisan.

There were the familiar roses around the door but this time they had been pruned and loved and encouraged to flourish. The whole scene was wondrous and surely the culmination of hard work and good management.

Jim had sold the top field and the spinney to developers who had built a small but exclusive housing estate. The rumour mill fantasised about how much Jim had received but it was never disclosed but must have been close to five million pounds. This sudden injection of cash into the estate changed both Jim and Charlotte's lives. Charlotte now owned the farmhouse and the rest of Windy Hill, now little more than a small holding. It had been completely refurbished from top to bottom and now pictures of it could sit very nicely in a home design magazine.

Jim, from the proceeds, had purchased another farm, further up the valley, where land prices were cheaper and had built a beautiful home of his own and was now very much a gentleman farmer and respected pillar of the community.

We had never really lost touch, though contact had been minimal, restricted to landmark texts about family and friends. Each message was as short and concise as the next. The content of the text was never the reason for sending. They were simply an acknowledgement of a shared experience, a single night, a childhood.

I followed the signs for parking and then the small, well-dressed crowd to an enormous marquee. I had not attended the ceremony, distance and travel times had made this impossible, but I was very much looking forward to reception and catching up with friends and extended family and slipping back into the character that I had perfected. The man that had moved away but had never forgotten his roots.

I had a splendid afternoon, listening to the speeches and stories of how Jim and his new wife, Cheryl had met and found myself getting quite emotional when missing pieces of my old friend's life journey were laid bare. I was too far from the top table to share any glances with Jim, who was busy, laughing at the anecdotes and gentle teasing of his best man. The only glimpse of our connection came when his best man asked if there was anyone who would like to say a few words. Only I saw the momentary glance around the room from Jim, only I saw, in that fleeting moment, the hurt that remained, hidden from the world. After the meal and chats and leg pulling from my table of memories, I went looking for Charlotte.

I had not picked her out of the crowd, and I couldn't let the day pass without putting an adult face to the little pigtailed seven-year-old, my last snapshot, that had taken far too much of my subconsciousness over the years. My quest was almost immediately over as an arm slipped around my waist from the rear. I turned to see the image of two people in one face.

There stood in front of me parts of the little girl I once knew and the rest was Mary, her mam.

It was incredible, my first thought was of the comet I had seen in a long, lost, previous life.

What followed was the most wonderful conversation with Charlotte about her mother and grandparents, all of whom she had never met, but had meant so much to me.

Charlotte was married to her university sweetheart, who seemed kind and clever and the furthest away from a farmer that you could imagine. They had a little girl together, Mary.

When I made this discovery, there seemed to be a gentle shift in the universe, a corrective movement that somehow made the world a little better. I felt warmed by the news. Charlotte was so very beautiful and the reincarnation of her mother but without the strain of perpetual anxiety from the constant cuckolding. My eyes tried not to linger on the small scar on her lip. It was faded now, barely visible and had become as insignificant as a childhood measle mark. She never knew about that night, she was too young to remember and the tale of it was never discussed by anyone, ever. She had been told it was a product of falling over on her roller skates when she was little, and this had been accepted without question. One constant and obvious omission was any mention of her father, a topic that neither of us was prepared to explore. When the conversation moved towards the refurbishment of the house, she became very animated indeed. "You must let me show you and you can meet Mary," squealed Charlotte, "She needs to wake up now or she won't sleep tonight." She pulled out a baby monitor from her bag. With that we headed for the house and toured the inside like I was a prospective buyer, which, in a distant dream world, I was. It took me only moments to fall back in love with Windy Hill Farm. Every aspect of its interior was new, apart from the beautiful staircase up the centre of the house which had been painstakingly returned to its former glory, hand polished and handsome.

The cracked and dirty flagstone floors were now removed and replaced with sandstone and heated from beneath. There was now a huge farmhouse kitchen with a nod to the past but containing every one of the modern kitchen appliances that they hadn't realised, until recently, they could not live without. The rest of the downstairs tour contained a large living room, an office, a dining room and a TV lounge, all perfectly falling onto the right side of style and opulence. As we returned to the hallway, I thanked Charlotte for the tour.

"Please let me show you the upstairs, we've reinstated the blocked windows and you can see clearly across the valley," pleaded Charlotte. I agreed immediately.

All thoughts of the old house had disappeared, I saw only the here and now, the happiness that this house would now bring its new family.

We headed up the wide staircase, the walls painted in cool grey with large and vivid paintings of the Gower Peninsular adorning the wall. I gave every one of them the credit they deserved, smoothing my hand along the beautiful wide handrail, feeling the moulding and the subtle undulation of its history, the sun rejoicing through the windows as we climbed. Then everything changed.

I heard a baby's voice. Quietly at first. It was coming from Charlotte's bag, from the baby monitor. I felt a wave of coldness creeping up my spine. I tried to ignore it. Charlotte smiled at me, knowing that Mary's awakening had perfect timing. As we climbed, the conversation was now one sided with me nodding at every description of every detail.

As we reached the second floor, the baby's cries intensified, and I felt a desperate need to run up the stairs rather than down. To find the baby, to take her in my arms and get out of here.

I settled myself, tried to re-establish the reality of the situation but I was not in this moment, I was being dragged back, back to a place I had taken twenty-four years to try to forget.

The Grandfather clock cuffed me around the ear even though it had long since been auctioned off to a new owner, but it was here, now, controlling every moment of the ascent.

"Are you ok?" said Charlotte, "You seem quiet." "I'm fine," I lied. "It's all just a bit overwhelming." Mary's voice was gently crying but all I could hear was Charlotte's voice screaming in fear, desperate to be saved, saved from… I couldn't let myself picture it again.

As we climbed the narrowed staircase of the top floor I was stopped in my tracks, the baby's voice was in stereo, from the monitor and the baby's room. The same room. I heard Charlotte's screams; I heard the clock. I saw the Grandfather Rat, its teeth, I heard its hellish screech, the gun shot, saw the blood, felt it splatter on my neck. "I've got to go, Charlotte, I'm not feeling well," I said as I turned and descended the staircase, trying not to run and embarrass myself completely. No protestations or queries came in response as I sensed her bewilderment. As I succumbed back to that night the screams of babies and shotguns and rats chased me down the staircase, I stepped over Dai's lifeless body as I went. This time he lay dead with the centre of his chest open and oozing with blood.

I got to the ground floor, there were people in the vestibule, so I headed to the back of the house, confused by the new layout which was now enveloped in an orangery. Through the doors and out into the sunlight, out of the house. I stood in the yard, now bathed in wedding flowers and summer colour. I felt the sweat dripping down my back, I tried to slow my breathing, tried to compose myself before making my excuses to leave. Calmer now I searched for the way back to the marquee or better the car park.

A soft, silent slipping away, I decided, was preferential to burdening these lovely people with my murderous melodrama. As I left the yard, I saw the barn, big and friendly and smiling for my attention. "I should leave with good thoughts," I said, silently to myself as I felt drawn to the entrance. I stood alone, this time not in the shadows but the airy, neat interior, smothered in the loving smell of its internal wooden structure. I imagined the fortress of straw, heard our voices inside, laughing our childhoods away.

I smelt the paraffin lamp, long since extinguished. I was lost in the moment that became endless minutes; I knew I was leaving but found it hard to go.

As I finally said goodbye to Windy Hill Farm for the last time, I felt someone take hold of my sleeve, gently and reassuringly. I didn't turn immediately; I knew who it was. My head dropped, I smiled and eventually turned to see it reflected in their face. It was Jim. "Game of darts?" he said. I laughed like a child and so, in turn, did he. We talked. Finally, we talked.

The memories that reunited us that day smelt of hay.

Messrs. Hughes, Morgan, Manley and Morgan

Megs knew I had a problem.

Even before we were married, she was aware of the dark secret I carried with me. She had struggled to accept it at first, she thought it was weird, creepy even. But being the person she is, she eventually came to terms with it. She adjusted our relationship to accommodate it, tried to ignore it at times but eventually realised the fact that it was just part of me, an integral component of who I am.

The fact was, I liked men, older men. Men with flat caps and nicotine-stained fingers. Men with baccy tins and pipes. Men who walked their dogs alone on a rainy Bank Holiday. I liked men who fished and made projects in their sheds, who smelt of oil and fixed mowers. I adored men with stories of bare-knuckle fights and pit prop failures. Those that had music in their hearts and coal dust in their pores.

When I moved to England, for the sake of love and longing, my tastes changed. There, I liked older men with plaid afternoon suits and final salary pension schemes. Those that played golf, wore cravats, and fed their cats with fish scraps bought especially from the monger.

Military men, time served loyal men with a lifetime of knowledge and a carriage clock to prove it. Rogues, scallywags, or family men with a life of pride kept steady with a walking stick. I sought out these men in a multitude of places and found them at the end of public bars, sitting alone in the corner with a half of bitter and a daily newspaper. At bus stops and on park benches. At the theatre and walking in the street. Such was my obsession that I even met them in doorways and underpasses. Dirty, smelly old men with a disdain for others, whose coats were never fastened, and their shoelaces never tied.

I knew I had an issue, an addiction really. There were times when I simply needed to feast. To make up for lost time, to take from them what I so desperately craved, their company. Very often we would walk into a pub or restaurant, stand at the lectern of judgement, manned by some power crazed pubescent, waiting to be seated and Megs would scan the room first, surveying the best seat to keep me out of harm's way. If a victim was spotted, she would sigh in resignation.

"Not tonight, Lynd, I'm not in the mood," a phrase I would become woefully familiar with. "Just five minutes, I promise," my stock reply. She said I was like a varicose vampire, addicted to blood flavoured with Ovaltine, St Bruno, and Port wine. The reality was I just liked to sit and listen, after the groundwork had been done and I had managed to secure a moment of their time.

Things subsided significantly the day I met Meg's Dad, Bob.

Our first encounter hardly got off on the right foot. It was my first visit to Meg's hometown of Kenilworth, and I was travelling up in my beige Mini Metro.

A babe magnet so lacking in powers of speed and attraction to the opposite sex that I always parked it at the far end of any car park or, if possible, behind a tree. It had broken down in Bideford-on-Avon, some twenty miles from Kenilworth and I had found a phone box to break the bad news to Megs. She had laughed at my predicament and said instantly, "It's fine, my dad will fetch you."

That always amazed me back then, that someone could depend on one person so emphatically, that they had someone in their lives that would stop everything, at the drop of a hat, to sort out their problems. To this day, it forms part of the reason I peel myself out of bed at some ungodly hour to answer the call of my reprobate offspring.

In just over half an hour, Megs and Bob had arrived. I had prepared for his annoyance of our first meeting, his disgruntlement. His "What the hell have you brought home now?" thoughts as he shook my hand, wanting to rip my arm off and beat me with the soggy end. But this didn't happen. I was greeted with the broadest smile and a gentle teasing of my situation. I could tell Bob had had a couple of beers. He had been summoned from his beloved golf club and was eager to return. It was the only folly that I ever saw in him. Like most men of his generation, he had a flagrant disregard for the drink-driving laws. His cohort had driven in the glorious days of "Mungo Jerry."

I was relieved to receive such a warm welcome and a little surprised. Not as surprised as I was that he intended to tow me for the twenty miles back to Kenilworth though. Unbeknown to Megs, I had not passed my test and had no insurance. It had started one night with an unchallenged trip to Tonna chippy and had spiralled out of control from there. We fixed the tow rope between the two cars, and we were off. Megs rode in her dad's car, a very sporty, executive style Toyota. Level three in the pecking order at the golf club, behind Aston Martins and Jags.

The journey was long, but the rope was not. After about a mile, I realised that Bob really was in a rush to get back to his "Pringle" clad mates at the golf club. After two miles, I became convinced that he had forgotten I was attached. Speeds reached fifty then sixty miles an hour as we sped through the darkness of the Warwickshire countryside. I was hovering on the brake constantly and trying to keep in his slipstream, I was terrified, and my stress levels were near boiling point as I tried desperately not to shunt him in the arse end of his car at every junction and roundabout. I became paranoid this was a test, a punishment for daring to suggest that my diminutive stature and lack of prospects was ever going to infect the purity of his gene pool, and this was his way of sorting the wheat from the "chav."

The truth, that I was unaware of, was that he was in a snooker tournament at the club, and he was on the table next. I also had not realised the sheer laidback-ness of the man. The "everything will be fine, don't worry," mantra that defined him. We arrived at Meg's driveway at top speed. Bob unhitched us and sped off to try and beat his best break of twenty-eight. He was dreadful at snooker. It once took me two hours to manufacture a victory for him when we played together. I fell onto the driveway, exhausted through my near-death anxiety.

Bob was so very easy to love, and it wasn't long before I was "our Lynd," in conversations and the way I was accepted into the family was both heart-warming and pivotal in my search to be a fully formed adult. He was tall, handsome, fair, wore fashionable spectacles of the day and it was always noted that he reminded people, who met him for the first time, of Michael Caine, a compliment he never tired of. To be in his stewardship was to induce feelings of safety and warmth, that nobody should ever get you down, that tomorrow would be another day, that life was too short. He was right on all counts. We lost Bob aged fifty-seven, just two years older than I am whilst writing this, after a surgeon had a bad day at the office. His loss was beyond the words I could ever attempt to place here and would affect Megs and I and our son, Jake, to this day and beyond. I suppose that my first day of true manhood corresponded with his passing. I realised what a thankless, terrifying honour it was to be the person who tries to fix the unfixable, rebuild the once mighty.

I gave it my best shot and others will be the judge of whether I have measured up or not. I have, however, tried, whenever possible, to be like Bob.

I hope my children read this book, though they will have to purchase it like everyone else - I am only financially obligated for the first eighteen years.

My school days were a powerful source of material, especially at Llangatwg Comprehensive.

They say these are the best years of your life and I am filled with sympathy for those that had a dreadful time, but for me they most definitely were.

By the time we had reached the fifth form we had all comfortably settled into our position in the school year. We all had a role to play, a stereotype to mould into. There were the swats, whose levels of achievement were without tint and whose success was guaranteed. There were the elite fashionistas, both boys and girls, who glided through the school with blemish free complexions, oozing sexual attraction and flaunting their futures in the faces of others. There were the quiet, studious ones who had yet to blossom but kept the secret to themselves that the world would, one day, be theirs. There were the ones that, however hard they tried, would always just fall short and a lifetime of "if only" beckoned from the shadows. There were the ones who had no chance whatsoever, who couldn't care less if they tried. Whose lives contained far too many distractions and missing parts to ever construct the foundations of a solid future.

We had the sporty ones, the aggressive, toughest in the school, ones. The untouchable girls that you dreamed of at night who were sprinkled with sugar and spice and all things nice. There was a place for everyone, and everyone knew their place.

I knew my place, but it was a little more complicated. I had a foot in many camps. I played rugby but was never at the top level in the school with the boys that had smashed through puberty like it was a forward line made up of boys who studied Latin and Drama. I was in the top class but was always mid table come the end of the season. I was nice looking but not handsome. I was clever but not gifted. I dressed nicely but my apparel lacked the logos of judgement that were so very important at that age. I was a Prefect but never in the running for Head boy or his Deputy. I was perfectly happy under the cover of, and in the company of, those daft enough to raise their heads above the parapet.

I was positive, popular in a larger sphere than most, noticed by more than most, I made people laugh and never once got my face smashed in. In school, at least. Llangatwg was great.

But like Ronnie Corbet before me, I knew my place.

I wasn't average, I was a bit better than that, but I knew I would never excel in any of the decathlon events that ruled the school. But like all rules, there are exceptions.

With the champions of all the disciplines decided, I was quite happy to trundle along and collect my exam results, make my Mam proud, then move on to whatever life had in store for me. There was an area of the school that I did stand out, but in a huge contradiction to the last statement, nobody had noticed. I loved woodwork classes. I had from the second year onwards gone to an evening class on a Wednesday night where I had built shelves, chess boards and key holders, tables, lamps, and snooker cues. I loved it and it provided me with oversized gifts for my Mam who, without complaint, tried to awkwardly accommodate them in our already cramped council house.

This careless accumulation of skills meant that by the end of my fourth year in the school I was the undisputed and undiscovered champion of the Craft department, resulting in me passing both my Woodwork and Metalwork O levels a year early with almost flying colours. I never made a fuss of this fact, never brought attention to it because, well, I was a bit embarrassed by it.

I am ashamed to say that, at that stage of my life, in the company I kept and the girls I aspired to snog, the Craft department was somewhere where the no-hopers hung out. The boys who would pass no exams other than a CSE in Woodwork or Metalwork and go on to make a perfectly good living and have satisfactory lives and eventually provide the school with offspring that too would get a CSE in Woodwork or even Home Economics. For me, it just wasn't sexy, and I was terrified it would affect my standings in the popularity polls.

Then they gave me an award.

"The Minchington Award for Excellence in Craft," my worst bloody nightmare. An award that had been forgotten about and probably found in the dark recesses of a long unopened cupboard and had last been presented in the sixties when Craft was "King of the Comp."

"Who shall we give it to? I know, let's give it to Lyndon. His life seems to be going ok. He desperately wants to have sex. Let's mess it all up for him, it will be hilarious." Said the smoke-filled staffroom, en masse.

So, there I stood on the stage, in front of everyone, accepting an award I didn't want in an assembly that didn't give a shit. I felt my physical attraction wane before their very eyes. I felt my teeth protrude, my hair adopt an unfashionable style and my acne, which had previously remained under control, spread bacterially across my petri dish face. This would set me back. "Mallet me round the back of the head now. For the love of linseed oil, end my misery."

I said to myself as I cowered off the stage and then went to my first lesson over at the Woodwork room. By first break and, after a healing dose of wood butchery, I had forgotten all about it. I looked out of the window and saw the two girls I had spent most time alone in my room with - they were never really there of course; it was always just me.

Elaine Lansdowne and Catherine Jones sauntered across to the Physics lab for their next lesson like they were riding on a cloud of desire. Sadly, one league above me, I looked longingly at their perfection, imagining what their hair would smell like as it bounced in slow motion as they walked arm in arm. As they disappeared around the corner, I had an idea. It would be a risk, but fortune never favoured those lacking in stupidity. I grabbed my trophy off the windowsill and kicked open the emergency doors at the back of the workshop as the two were passing by.

111

A little startled, they looked up to see me standing with mock smugness, "The Minchington" proudly in my hands.

"Welcome to my parlour, said the spider to the fly," I said alluringly, dancing my eyebrows and pursing my lips like Windsor Davies, having heard that phrase somewhere before and believing it to be funny in this situation. It seemed I had chosen well as they both burst into laughter and threw their heads back as they hurried away, looking back, and giggling as they went. Off I trotted to double Maths.

At the end of the school day, I had a wink and a nod from Menna Berryman, probably my favourite girl in the entire school and the only one I could truly call my friend. Menna was the fixer in the school and was responsible for the entire dating scene.

She was a matchmaker with mysterious powers that I was sure were inherited from a long line of mystical ancestors.

She informed me that Elaine thought I was funny and wanted to know if I would dance with her at the Fifth Form Disco that was looming in a couple of weeks.

"Would I? I'll dance her bloody legs off," I squealed, losing grasp on reality, and missing the point completely. "Oh shit," said Menna, shaking her head as she walked away, doubting her gift for once. And so that signified my promotion into the first division of Llangatwg School. I was then invited to the best parties and had the opportunity to make girls laugh I had previously only gazed upon from afar. I had arrived, I was part of the top echelons of year five superstars, I had made it.

Of course, It wasn't long before I'd cocked it up completely when Rebecca Britzman cut her lip on my loosely fitting temporary denture whilst in the throes of a particularly passionate snog. But while it lasted, I soared amongst the beautiful people, walked with the Gods clad in "Slazenger," "Levi" and "Wrangler." Heady days indeed.

Llangatwg had the greatest names for its teachers. Each one honed by some unnamed heroes from the distant past. Some nicknames were twenty years old and could be used to describe a particular teacher to our parents even and they would instantly know who you were talking about due to the fact they had taught your older siblings or even themselves. We had Penguin from Physics, who waddled like his Gotham City cousin. Egghead from Maths, because of his parabolic dome. Jesus Johnson from Religious Education, just because he had a beard. Mrs Twizzle from Welsh was so thin there was a rumour put around that she was pregnant, but it was deemed a false alarm when we discovered she had simply swallowed a pickled onion. We had Dai Shrub from Horticulture and my personal favourite was Bummer Hughes from Chemistry who, one day, made the monumental mistake of bringing his wife's brightly coloured umbrella to school.

There were four teachers that I spent most time with. They were all, unsurprisingly, from the Craft Department. Messrs Hughes, Morgan, Manley and Morgan. These men did more to mould me into the young man I became than any before.

MISTER HUGHES.

Mr Hughes was known to the school as "Yosser," due to his resemblance to Bernard Hill who played "Yosser Hughes" in Alan Bleasdale's hard hitting TV drama of the day "Boys from the Black Stuff." Never had a nickname been so perfectly appropriate. It gave Mr Hughes' standing in the school a little boost when so many others do the exact opposite. He was a disciplinarian, beyond compare and this moniker gave him an edge of danger and madness that saw his reputation and legacy become set in stone. He had had a previous career as a metal fabricator before retraining as a teacher, spurred on by his sister and brother-in-law Mr and Mrs Morris, who also worked in the school as teachers. Mr Morris was Head of the Craft Department.

Mr Hughes taught Metalwork at the school but also ran a woodwork evening class on a Wednesday night. He seemed to me to be always on a path of self-improvement.

He was well read and aspired to emulate Mr Morris, who was regarded as a craftsman beyond comparison. Mr Morris once went to visit the violin making World Championship in Switzerland and took a violin he had made to get some advice on. He was encouraged to enter his instrument in the competition and came third overall. Mr Morris was a very nice man and missed this shortlist by a whisker. Mr Hughes was respected by those that aspired to learn and feared by those that didn't. He was a "no nonsense", "take it or leave it", "GET OUT!!" sort of a bloke but being in his tutelage was never a chore and, almost always, a pleasure.

I never fell for the fire in his eyes, "do as I say," facade. I was well-versed in the world of real violence, real and instant fear, so, very quickly, I saw the kindness in his eyes, the softness in his manner, but I had earned it and it didn't come cheap. Four years of evening classes, every Wednesday night. Two miles there and two back in the wind, rain, and snow. I never missed a night. Well, only one.

Dai Price was the only other person that came anywhere close to full attendance, but he didn't like the rain even though he lived only three hundred yards from the school. One time, only I had succumbed to the lurex allure of the school disco, the only time it was ever on a Wednesday night.

There was no way of letting Mr Hughes know without popping in but him seeing me in my bri-nylon shell suit and string vest was never an option. The next day I was called to his office and asked, "Where were you last night?" "At the school disco, Sir," I said sheepishly, "It was a last-minute thing." "Mmm... Well, Dai Price made it, no problem."

"I don't think Dai Price is the disco dancing sort, Sir," I offered, hoping to lighten the mood. "Oh, and you are, are you Lyndon?

114

Well, you won't mind giving me a demonstration then, will you?" he said smoothly, folding his arms and leaning back in his captain's chair. I had two choices here. Step up or step out. I was always a risk taker and the delicious pay off was too much to resist. What followed was my minute-long, party piece of robotic, moonwalking, Marcel Marceau inspired dance routine that culminated in a full three-hundred-and-sixty-degree spin and the final pose of me holding my chin whilst looking nonchalantly towards the horizon. There was silence, then the only time I had ever witnessed Mr Hughes roar with laughter. He threw his head back and I loved the way he laughed. Mid-stream he said, "Go on, you daft bugger, clear off, I'll see you Wednesday." I could still hear him laughing as I walked down the corridor.

MISTER MORGAN (Woodwork).

Mr B J Morgan was a living, breathing institution. He was our Woodwork teacher and quite honestly one of the funniest men to ever draw breath. Like all masters of mirth, he was always in total control. Never once did I hear him raise his voice, not once did I see him let a situation arise that he needed to. He was bald on top, but his hairstyle of choice saw a band of brown hair skirt the perimeter of his head, tempting such nicknames as "BJ the Clown." But they never arose, such was the love we had for the man. Even his hilarious initials were not highlighted in derision due mostly to the fact that the name, in the early Eighties, for "fellatio" had not yet morphed into that particular acronym.

He sported a rather dashing goatee and always wore his glasses on his head. He had total mild manipulation over his classes through cleverly timed teasing, creating an atmosphere of inclusion and building team spirit and self-confidence. His registers were legendary and almost obliterated absenteeism in his lessons.

I can recite part of our class register verbatim and his remarks to it.

Phil Ravioli?	(Paul Feneroli)	"Yes Sir."
Gerald Fitz Michael?	(Michael Fitz Gerald)	"Yes Sir"
Tony Boloni?	(Anthony Mahoney)	"Yes Sir."
London Geriatric?	(Lyndon Jeremiah)	"Yes Sir."
Trevor Bird?		"Yes Sir"
"Speak up Bird, I'm a trifle deaf."		"YES SIR."
Rhys Marconi?		"YES SIR."
"Turn it down, Marconi."		"Sorry, Sir."

And so, it continued. It was hilarious and made each one of us laugh and feel like we were all included in his obtuse slant on the world. The only person in the class who was never awarded a pseudonym was Ivor Dichard, who had unfortunately taken on his stepfather's name and Mr Morgan said he had suffered enough. To me, it was like being in the presence of Spike Milligan or Peter Sellers. His surreal guise was so very clever, and we were absorbing the knowledge without knowing it.

If a mortise and tenon was badly fitting, he would shout into the gap "Hello," then like a skilled ventriloquist an echo could be heard from the back of his throat, "H-e-l-l-o, h-e-l-l-o," petering off in volume. Genius.

He had a little ditty for any pupil who had used too much glue in a dovetail joint that was not quite tight enough.

"If, at first it does not fit, fill it up with muck and shh... sawdust." Inspired.

But if you ever produced a piece of work that was of an excellent standard he would stop the class, gather them around and wait for silence.

He would then rotate his shoulders, then his neck, pretending it clicked three times with more ventriloquism, then place his glasses on his nose and examine your work. We hung in a quiet collective, waiting for his verdict, craving the comedy.

He would then put his glasses back on his head, pinch his nose and pretend to cry. "This is my last day at work boys, I can teach you no more," as his mock tears continued. Then he would pull himself together instantly and say, "Well done, Grasshopper," in a Chinese accent, stolen from the TV show "Kung Fu." He always finished with a casual wink. And what a wink it was.

MISTER MANLEY.

Mr Manley was a man of the times. Unlike the other teachers of practical subjects, he was cool and trendy. He taught Motor Mechanics and even though I was never in any of his classes I knew him well through the Friday evenings he gave up whilst running the Youth Club.

He loved cars and usually had the best one in the school. Never the newest, but the best. He had a red Porsche once and it elevated him to superstar status in the school. He had a decade appropriate hairstyle and a tache to rival the likes of Tom Selleck or Freddie Mercury. He had a pretend romance with Miss Jean Foulkes that nobody believed but put them both on the very top of the favourite teacher list within the school.

"Hello Miss Foulkes." Followed by, "Well, hello Mr Manley," was enough to send the whole corridor or classroom or even the entire assembly hall into a hysteria of whistles and cheers. It was a wonderful ruse.

Youth Club was amazing fun and a time when you could chill with your friends without the bus stop chill of November. We had film nights when we put the various arrays of old sofas on tables at the back, creating two tier seating to rival the Rank Cinema on Windsor Road.

We watched age-inappropriate videos like "The Wanderers," "The Warriors," and "Death Race 2000." We had a pool table, flick football and a tabletop Space Invaders machine. We bought "Panda Pops," "Rainbow Drops", "Refreshers" and "Black Jacks." Sometimes with our pocket money and sometimes on tick.

It was seven o'clock till ten every Friday night, and if there were any fights to be had they were sorted only after we had waved Mr Manley home as he pulled away in his latest dream machine.

It was a massive undertaking to devote so much of his time for the kids of Cilfrew, Cadoxton and Aberdulais, but we saw no complaints from him as we mercilessly took advantage of his kindness.

He laughed when we sneaked out to the phone box to ring the club that made him run to the office only to find we had superglued the Trimphone receiver in place. He took it on the chin with every loss at pool and ran a circuit of victory around the dance floor with every win.

Of all the teachers I knew, he understood how hard it was for some kids, the battles they fought and the huge obstacles they had to overcome every day of their lives. There was no fake concern, no obligatory duty, just kindness and a commitment to help. He knew where most of us would be if we were not in the Youth Club and he knew what we would be doing and the trouble it would lead to. The pinnacle of membership at the club was the disco which happened once a term.

This gathered a much larger crowd, and the thirty pence entrance fee was snapped up like spare dinner tickets. It was always Mr Manley who ran the decks with the panache of a Radio One DJ. He made DLT and Tony Blackburn seem like novices as he stood resplendent in flares and cheesecloth. He would effortlessly transport you to a steamy world of wild romance.

Those nights saw the start of loves that could last a lifetime and I can testify to many that are still going strong today. They certainly provided future pupils of the school that would go on to benefit from his kindness.

The memory of Mr Manley and Miss Foulkes dancing, in close embrace, to "Zoom," by "Fat Larry's Band," whilst, unnoticed by most, Mrs Manley and the current beau of Miss Foulkes looked on with affection, will always glow warmly in my heart. Mr Manley's legacy was assured, and he can seldom go out in public without the adoration of his flock.

It is my hope that he never has to buy a pint some nights and that people remember him with the same loving affection that I do. Mr Manley was an extraordinary teacher and is a lovely, lovely man.

MR MORGAN (Tech Drawing).

Sure, as there is light, there is always darkness. Whenever there is laughter, tears are sure to follow. For all that is good in the world there is undeniably and unequivocally evil.

Mr Morgan was all of these and more. He was the most despised teacher in the school and the most feared. Unlike other disciplinarians in the school, he was not in control of his temper and for the lightest of reasons he would lash out with a smack around your head or a swift kick in the shins. He was known as "Bilko" as he had a passing resemblance to Phil Silvers who played "Sgt Bilko," in "The Phil Silvers Show." I was aware of his nickname well before catching the black and white American show on late night TV and was shocked to see his doppelgänger with such an array of facial expressions. I had seen our Bilko with only one. Anger.

His lessons were dull and were so lacking in joy that the hour would pass like a month of Thursday afternoons, period four. Getting to the end of his lesson unscathed was akin to a death row pardon or the misdiagnosis of a terminal disease.

We left the room feeling we had survived a hostage situation, and all refused to acknowledge that next week we would have to do it all again. He was a tank-topped tyrant with a single egg-stained tie to his name.

He smelt of oil, fags and body odour and had the nose blindness of someone who lived alone. His hands were hairy and hid the most cumbersome left-footed fingers I had ever seen. He never visited the board without dropping something and would snap a virgin chalk as soon as black met white. He would leave the room at least once every lesson for a sneaky cigarette in the boiler room opposite his classroom and this gave Anthony Mahoney (Tony Boloni) the chance to end our relieved chatter with instant fear with an uncanny impression of him.

God only knows how this never caught us out. His room was strewn with items he had taken apart and would never function again. He bragged of jobs he had undertaken but there was never any proof of their satisfactory completion. He claimed to have taught most of the current staff all they knew yet I never once saw him in the workshop, and he never shared his break times with other members of staff.

Bilko lamented the demise of British industry and banged on about the times when "Britannia ruled the waves, the world and the wogs."

He would hold items in the air and brag of the superb quality of British craftsmanship, having never contributed to a single widget. One item that he had a particular affection for was his beloved pencil sharpener that sat pride of place clamped to his desk.

"I have had this pencil sharpener for forty years, boys," and he would re-sharpen a pencil in celebration to literally prove his point. He would unclamp it and wax lyrical about the accuracy of the components, the perfection of the body casting and the timeless edge of the self-sharpening blades.

"Like me, boys, it's as good now as it was forty years ago," he would say, congratulating himself on his own oration.

My God, it was so satisfying to be one of the six boys hiding in the Art block with the windows open to hear the crunch of that pencil sharpener succumb to the weight of his back tyre as he reversed out of his parking space two minutes after the school bell had sounded, with the bonus of a puncture to boot. He had told that boring story to every class for the last twenty years and had no way of tracking down who the culprits were. Like pimpernels in a variety of primary colours, our secret was safe.

In another lesson, with another group, on another day, sometime in the future, a man had wandered into the Tech Drawing room when one of Bilko's torture sessions was in full flow. The man was in work shorts, rigger boots and a high visibility vest.

The class stopped, as did Bilko, not recognising the man or the impending event that was soon to unravel. The man looked to the back of the class and sought out one of the boys.

"Is this him, Son?" said the man. "Yes, Dad," said the boy. The man approached Bilko and proceeded to beat him to the floor with a series of full-blooded head smacks and shin kicks, whilst asking him, rather politely under the circumstances, how he liked it? The man and his son then left and headed to the headmaster's office. The incident was never reported, and no complaint was ever made.

In 1986, corporal punishment by a teacher was abolished in schools in England and Wales.

In 1993, it became a criminal offence. In British prisons, it had not been tolerated since 1962.

Bilko continued to teach but his pupils no longer feared him... In the Spring of 1992, I returned to Llangatwg School as a student teacher as part of my Post Graduate Certificate in Education.

I had passed my Degree in Three-Dimensional Design with flightless colours and the Education Department was handing out grants as an incentive to take up the course.

Another year at university? More football, rugby, and international weekends in Cardiff? More parties with double the budget? It was quite a decision. I left the registration office with an optimistic outlook and the registrar's bloodied hand between my teeth as I looked forward to another adventure and hopefully a valuable qualification at the end of it.

As part of the course, I had to complete an eight-week teaching practice at a local school in Newport. True to form, I had not got my paperwork in on time and all the schools were full and so I had the blinding idea of asking if I could stay at home in Neath for a while and do my teaching practice at Llangatwg School. A couple of phone calls later, it was all arranged.

My nostalgic journey to school on my first morning was to be very eventful. For old times' sake I called in to the village shop for a packet of "Toffos" for my break. Old habits and all that. The place had not changed much in my three years away and I marvelled at the memories. I was a little surprised to see a new proprietor in the shop.

The Biggs Family, it seemed, had sold up and were chewing the sweet grass of success in pastures, new. The recent addition to the village seemed friendly as I introduced myself as Angela's boy.

I recognised a Brummie accent as I bid him farewell and turned to leave the shop, but not before noticing a collection of white "penny sweet" bags lined up on the side of the till. Each one had three cigarettes inside and there was a small sticker with "30p a bag" next to them. I enquired about the items for sale and without an ounce of embarrassment he explained that the kids in Cilfrew couldn't afford a full pack of cigarettes and so this was his way of making them more available.

I looked at his face and saw the expression of someone who considered his actions as kind and generous, saintly even. We then had a gentlemanly conversation regarding the fact that I would now be teaching at the school and how uncomfortable I felt about this unusual rebranding of his age sensitive merchandise. He took the opposite view and put his argument across with good grace and manners. This continued for a few minutes with no appeasement on either side but, after banging his head on the shop counter three times, he seemed to share my point of view almost immediately.

By Jove, it felt good to be home.

It was with a mixture of excitement and nerves as I approached the Craft block, or as it was now called, The Craft, Design and Technology Department. This had been shortened to the CDT block and for me signified the beginning of a changing of the guard in Education.

The start of it was acronyms, bloody pointless, lazy arse, "I am a bit more important than you because I took the first letter from a group of random words and formed them into a word that makes no sense," bloody acronyms. Apart from that, it had changed very little except for a few additional Portacabins and a long overdue paint job. Inside the double doors, everything felt weirdly smaller, not by much, but by about ten percent. The place was brighter, less cluttered and the walls were adorned with posters and guides showing the way into the exciting new decade. I knew the small staff area was where the Craft teachers gathered for their pre-lesson cup of tea and so headed there, knocked and went in.

There before me were my favourite three teachers. Mr Hughes, Mr Manley and Mr Morgan (Woodwork). They all sat around a small table busy with something or other. Mr Morgan was reading the paper, Mr Hughes seemed to be writing in a notebook and Mr Manley was listening to music on his headphones. "Good morning," I said cheerfully, expecting the world but receiving none of it.

They all sat at the table, not acknowledging my, less than, prodigal return. "Morning all," I persisted, hoping they hadn't heard me the first time. Still no answer. I was crestfallen. I expected to be received with open arms, with the parade of a returning hero. But nothing.

Then Mr Hughes spoke. "So, you are the new student then, are you?" "Yes Sir," I replied. Old habits and all that. "Well, stick the kettle on, there's a good fellow," piped Mr Morgan. Mr Manley continued nodding his head to the music. And that's what I did, put the kettle on and regretted going there that morning, organising my teaching practice in the first place, and even enrolling on the course.

These were the only reasons I had considered teaching in the first place and none of them remembered me. I was truly and utterly gutted.

"One question for you, Student," enquired Mr Hughes, without looking at me and focussing on his notebook. "Yes Sir," I repeated. There was a long pause. Everyone continued to be busy doing nothing. I stood waiting uncomfortably in the silence. Then Mr Hughes looked at me, raised his glasses and said, "How is your Disco dancing going?"

With that they burst into laughter and got up to greet me, shaking my hand and patting me on the back. I noticed then that Mr Morgan's newspaper had been upside down and Mr Manley's headphones had been plugged into the teapot.

They had got me, well and truly stitched me up, done me up like a kipper and what a wonderful honour it was. A beautiful moment I will never forget.

It turned out Mr Hughes was now Head of Department. Mr Morgan was retiring that year and Mr Manley was Deputy Headmaster no less.

I had the most marvellous experience in those eight weeks, sharing time with those three.

I taught with Mr Hughes, which brought back fond memories and Mr Morgan, which was as good as it ever was. Whether it was because of my return or because he had done it naturally, Mr Morgan had a new repertoire as good as the original. I did however reinstate some old classics like,

"H-e-l-l-o, h-e-l-l-o...." and, "If at first it does not fit..." to Mr Morgan's delight.

Mr Manley coached me on interview technique in preparation of some upcoming teaching jobs and shed common sense on a situation with a female pupil that could so easily have caught out a young, naive student with the best intentions but a crushing lack of experience in such matters. By the end of my first week, I could put it off no longer. I asked if I could take a few lessons with Bilko. It was with a mixture of curiosity and my need to face my demons that I went to see to discuss taking a few lessons off his hands. He was not the man I was expecting to see. It was eight years since I was last at Llangatwg, but the years had not been kind to him. He looked to have aged by twenty years or more and his manner was slower and less interested in life. His nerves had taken over his body and the cup rattled in the much-needed saucer as he tried to drink it. He knew my name but didn't recognise me, why would he? I was just cannon-fodder to him as he rampaged through his world of being right. Where no one cared enough to tell him he was not. He was thin and constantly wore his flat cap like he really didn't want to settle. His lessons were shambolic and loud, and I was able to make an instant connection with his classes by using the techniques I had learned from the others. He was the one that benefited most from my visit, and he was to be my harshest critic, giving me less than glowing reports in contrast to the others. He seemed broken by the fact that he had no control or respect from his pupils. He had not invested his time, his care and his love into a profession that will give you a return on your investment larger than you could imagine.

His countdown clock had started to tick the day he started teaching and he had watched it every day since. His hours were nearly up and as far as he was concerned, good riddance. Shortly after I left to return to university, Bilko retired. His retirement was short and lonely, and I heard he had passed away a couple of years later. The pension he had put so much importance on to suffer a life of misery for, remained unused and he missed any opportunity he may have had to give his possessions to someone dear. He was never missed and remembered only by those with little good to say.

I left my teaching practice at Llangatwg with mixed feelings. I saw the way teaching was going and I didn't like it. It felt that this was the tail end of a golden time, that we would never see again. I would go on to be a teacher for eight years before starting my own bespoke furniture making business, employing twenty-six people at its height.

I was to return to teaching later in life, whilst continuing my long-denied love of writing. I look back on my school days and realise everything that I needed for life was taught at that school and was so very lucky to have flourished in its warm embrace. I remember the last words Mr Morgan (Woodwork) said to me on my last day of teaching   practice.

"Well done, Grasshopper." This time without the accent.

I hopped happily off into the long grass and was never seen again.

126

Finding Albert

"Jeremiah. You've got no skill; you have the speed of a sloth, and you pass the ball like your boots are tied together. The only reason you are in this team is because you have a 'bit of dog', don't forget that."

Big Lou's words echoed in my head like I was sitting in a barrel. I had mildly celebrated an outrageous punt at goal which had whistled into the top corner at the last throes of training that Wednesday afternoon and it had seemed to piss him off, but the thing was, I loved it, I always had. I knew I was in the team by the skin of my teeth and that if there was any other viable alternative I would be back on the bench, because Lou was right; I wasn't as good as the other players, it was true.

I had played against most of them for years in the junior section of the Neath League and they were the best players of sides like Neath Boys Club, Giant's Grave and Salvo F.C. They were the best sides in the league, all brought together to represent Neath College and they were a great side.

Playing for Neath College and winning the Welsh College Championship meant more to me than the rest. For them, this was just part of the many trophies and accolades they would win. For me, this would be it, the pinnacle.

I had always played for my village side, Cilfrew Rovers, and had, since the age of fifteen, been a regular in the first team. I was the youngest player to get picked for the first eleven, snatching the record from, one footed wonder and monkey impersonator, Simon Evans.

For two whole seasons I was kicked the shit out of, by every pot-bellied has-been and club footed inbred in the league.

The only advantage to this, of course, was, whilst my college teammates were representing West Glamorgan and West Wales at under 18's level, I was getting my armpit hair pulled and my balls squeezed by the toothless left back from Upper Cwmtwrch and by the time I got to Neath Tertiary College I was used to the onslaught of dirty tricks and underhand tactics, like when the half back for Cwmtawe had hidden his sovereign ring from the referee by turning inside his fist, only to turn it out the right way and gash me over the eyebrow during a corner. A knob of Vaseline, some gauze, held in place with black insulation tape, and I was pushed back onto the pitch.

I had been teased, taunted, and lovingly tortured by serious purveyors of the artform at Cilfrew Rovers. I had known them most of my life and had watched them every Saturday since I was six years old. I had been cold showered, had my underpants sprayed with "Deep Heat" and pushed naked outside the away supporters' end until I had finally earned my stripes as a fully-fledged "Rover".

The team hadn't really changed over the years, apart from every couple of seasons someone would get just a little bit too old or fat or both and retire to the first aid box carrier or putting up the nets. Most were in their late thirties and some in their forties, but they all knew their positions and what it took to win. We were considered, without rivals, the dirtiest and most hated team in the Neath League.

My job was to keep out of trouble, stay alive and stick the ball in the net if we ever got a chance in the opposition box, which would be only a handful of times in each match. They smoked fags at half time and drank lager from cans. They urinated in bushes and changed their antique, unwashed jockstraps in full view of the ladies in the crowd and flicked their fags skywards as they belched their way onto the pitch for the second half.

They were, without doubt, an absolute disgrace and I loved every one of them and they loved me.

The same blokes that set fire to my Christmas socks on Boxing Day, in our annual piss-up, were the same ones that regularly smashed someone's face in or kneed them in the bollocks if anyone ever caught me with a late tackle.

Big Lou was a man mountain. If that mountain was part of the miniature railway at Barry Butlins. He stood at five foot nothing and sported a child's tracksuit from Woolworths. He wore aviator sunglasses day and night, inside and out and had a seventies mullet and porn star moustache. I saw him clean his glasses at a dreadful league match in Swansea once and they looked like piss holes in the snow. He was feared by some of the boys but to me he was like a character from Michael Bentine's "Potty Time" or a gonk you win at Neath Fair.

He was blessed with the best college side in a generation and wasted no time in taking the entire credit for it. He had, what most people consider to be, the ten greatest players that had ever represented the college and time would see several of them go on and play for Swansea, Cardiff, Birmingham, and Arsenal. His problem was that he never had a left winger, not one. The gulf between his prized squad and the "also-rans" was vast, but I was the best of the rest and there was nothing he could do about it. I found it hilarious, the boys in the team even more so. We were all mates and they accepted me with open arms. The irony was they could have beaten anyone with ten men anyway, so it didn't matter who played left wing, but Big Lou's campaign of relentless derision made them get behind me. "Bit harsh Lou", said one, "Give it a rest Lou," said another. The fact I laughed at him when he slagged me off didn't do anything for my cause. I did, however, have several advantages that had supercharged my rather average comparative skills.

Firstly, I was used to playing at senior level, basic though it was. I was body hardened, like a gladiator with shin pads. Secondly, I never gave up.

I chased everything down, every lost cause, every pass back, I ran and ran, hoping for a mistake or a miscalculation by the opposition. Anyone watching me for a snapshot in a game would see me being beaten mercilessly by slick passing and skilful defenders, but tirelessly I continued. Then there was the unexplainable. The gift, the magic.

I was the luckiest player that had ever lived. I was, I never understood it or questioned it. The less I cared about it the luckier I became. There had been too many examples to not accept this phenomenon that only I had realised. I had hit the post only to score off the back of the keeper's head. On a different occasion, I had wellied it from outside the box, putting a Brazilian spin on the ball, simply because I hadn't done my lace up. I had headed a goal from a blasted free kick when all I was trying to do was get out of the way.

It got to the point that I knew I would get several chances in a game and so I just did my job until the chance arose and I knew it would go in. It wasn't arrogance, it was just luck, pure luck. This, more than anything else, really pissed Big Lou off. This together with my average height, my roguish good looks and my devil may care attitude really seemed to annoy him, plus, Big Lou hated Cilfrew Rovers and everything they stood for.

At the time, I had no idea why.

As we walked to the changing room that afternoon, talk moved to the semi-final home game tomorrow afternoon against Cardiff College. We had never played them before but beating them would take us to our first Welsh College final in ten years. The team sheet would be up before the game.

"Don't be late," said Big Lou collectively. "Jeremiah, you'll be on the bench tomorrow," and he was away, into his faded red Sirocco with the cushion on the seat that was moved forward so he could see through the gaps in the steering wheel. "Just another shit remark from Big Lou, true to form."

I thought nothing else of it and headed towards the bus stop, then home on the fifty-seven.

Big Lou pulled alongside me with his window down, "Kajagoogoo" playing loudly on his tape deck.

"See you, Lou," I said, slightly stooping to see inside the tobacco smoke filled interior of the car. "Typical Jeremiah," came a voice through the smoke, then the window wound up in three jerking stages as the handle was turned on the inside of the door. When this was complete, the car sped away.

That last remark had bothered me, I thought it over on the way home on the bus. I had looked up my name many times and all its various connotations. Its biblical references etc. I knew that one translation of my name was "a person who habitually prophesies doom." He didn't mean that surely? I decided I was overthinking it. That was far too highbrow for Big Lou. He had a Betamax copy of "Confession of a Driving Instructor" on his dashboard. It's just that he seemed to make it personal, that was all. "Strange", I thought, I didn't know any other Jeremiahs and so I had no idea if I was a typical one or not. I'd had the name all my life and in the land of Jenkins, Evans, Davies, and Jones it had been a tough gig at times. If it wasn't for Benedict Pulford, I would have got a lot more grief than I did at Primary School. Poor old "Bentdick Pullfart".

I was early to the game the next day after clearing it with Mr Davies, my Design Teacher. A man so entirely good that kindness seemed to surround him like a "Ready Brek" glow. The team sheet was up and as threatened, my name was down as a single substitute for the afternoon. Immediately, I looked to see who was playing at left wing, I was perplexed and angry to see it was left blank. There was no name written in that position. "What was this?" I thought, "What was Big Lou up to now?"

I went for a walk around the sportsground trying to get my head around what was going on.

By the time I got back the changing room was full and the away team had arrived. I entered the affray quietly and sat beneath a peg. The team was busy changing and there was the familiar big match excitement in the air. I glanced at the familiar faces, all going through their routines and warmups.

In walked Big Lou, his tiny little movements exaggerated by his proximity to those of average height and above. "Ok lads, I've got a little surprise for you, we've got a special guest star today. Come on in, sunshine."

There was a hushed silence and into the changing room walked the very opposite of sunshine, a presence so dark and sinister that the whole team stood agog. Some of the boys sat down, others turned away and the remainder either shook their heads or stood open mouthed. Into the centre of the room, strode Jimmy Gimson. "All right, shitheads," he shouted to all and nobody.

Jimmy was known to all of us. He was a great footballer, a legend really, but universally hated by all that knew him. Gimson had been on the books at Swansea City but got thrown out because, not only had he gone to Baron's Nightclub on the Friday night before a reserve game, but he had glassed an unsuspecting reveller in the process, scarring him for life. Jimmy had done six months in a Borstal, which, by the looks of things, had had no positive effect whatsoever.

He was now playing semi-pro for Merthyr Tydfil and working as an apprentice for Neath Borough Council, which was, I presumed, how Big Lou had managed to secure his services, due to his day release at the college.

I had never seen him in the flesh before, but I knew all about him. Gimson was a man/boy. At only seventeen, he was six foot two and as broad as a bus with shoulders like a pylon.

He was one of the ugliest humans I had ever seen, his ginger, shoulder length ringlets framed a skin tone akin to a corned beef hash.

He sweated profusely and his thick gold neck chain sparkled unconvincingly along with the hooped earring in each ear.

His self-adorned hands spelled out "Love" and "Hate". I noticed immediately that the "E" on "Hate" had been cocked up and looked more like an "S". I thought, "He should have been an apprentice milliner," but I decided not to mention it.

His forehead was enormous, which paled into insignificance next to his protruding chin, which was cleft like a toast rack and covered in angry boils shouting for their fifteen minutes of fame.

Quite frankly, the sight of him frightened the dear life out of me and, as I surveyed the bereavement ridden room, I don't think I was alone in that appraisal. "Jimmy will be captain today and he will have a roving role across the pitch. Richard, give him the armband. Campese, you will go out on the left. One game plan today, lads, give the ball to Jimmy!" Richard was our captain, and he was the best player in our side. He was always last out of defence, always encouraging and never made a mistake. He oozed leadership through every pore and was very much in the mould of the great Bobby Moore.

To his absolute credit and faultless sportsmanship, he removed his armband and handed it to Gimson, "Welcome, Jimmy," he said, looking him straight in the eyes. Gimson just nodded and continued chewing his gum as he took the accolade with no class whatsoever. Formalities completed, we all changed and headed out of the changing rooms with a roar.

We were decked out in our traditional red and black vertical stripes with black shorts and socks. Gimson spoiled the whole ensemble with his orange shorts and socks, strobing hideously in contrast to his pasty white yet massive thighs.

We were good anyway, but with Gimson this would surely be a walk over. I slipped on a rather musty training top drenched with the aroma of what could have been and followed the team out with the water bottles and first aid kit. There would be no game time for me today. Big Lou never made any changes whilst we were in front, he had no feelings of inclusion for his substitutes, no "give the lad a run out", no "go on son, enjoy".

As I was the last of our team to leave the changing rooms I stood and watched as Cardiff College noisily left their temporary domain in "Bluebird" blue. Out came the team, exactly as you'd expect. About half a dozen youths in their prime, lithe, chunky, and almost the exact reflection in size and stature of our team with varying heights, hair colour and body types. Then the next three players in the line-up streaming past me were black. I stood and watched, glued to the spot, rooted to the paving slabs outside the sports hall with the clickety clack of studs tap dancing a tune in my head. I had never seen a black person before, not in real life, on TV yes, but not in Neath, not in my world. They were all huge, slender and muscular. I remember thinking how magnificent they looked, the tone of their skin, the lack of blemishes, their elegance and grace as they seemed to exude confidence and health. The tightness of their haircuts and the unfamiliar pattern of its growth. They must have been amused by the absurdness of my stare or maybe they were used to it. The tops of their legs reached somewhere between my elbow and shoulders. I felt part-grown and stunted.

"Good luck today, mate," said the middle one in a rich Cardiff accent with the broadest of smiles. My attempt at a response was not forthcoming, then they were gone, pitch-ward. The three laughing and joking together as they turned to all witness my witless lack of worldly wisdom. By the time I got to the pitch side, both teams had warmed up and Gimson, the ref and one of the black players were tossing a coin. We kept our respective ends of the pitch and kick-off got underway.

What happened in the first half was horrible. Gimson basically ran around the park demanding the ball constantly with the continual endorsement of Big Lou. Gone was the tight organisation, the discipline and rhythmic passing we were known for. Gimson knocked our own players off the ball in his greediness for glory.

He took every freekick and remonstrated tirelessly with the referee on every minor altercation. He abused every player on both sides and still Big Lou shouted, "Get the ball to Jimmy". Cardiff in contrast were professional, controlled, and organised. Their calm approach to the game was starting to pay off with a few near chances, extinguished only by our decorated goalkeeper, Jones. In the run up to halftime we were starting to panic and just about everyone on our team were making mistakes, time after time. The relief of the half time whistle was palpable, and we headed to our touchline with our heads down. The only noise was coming from Gimson, who was spewing insults to all and sundry. Big Lou received the baton of abuse and ran with it. He tore apart nearly everyone on the team and continued with his instruction to get the ball to Gimson.

He even looked at me at one stage but try as he might, he couldn't pin any blame on me. I momentarily saw my own reflection in his "Reactolite" sunglasses as he turned away.

As the teams ran back on the pitch Gimson shouted, without any regard for who heard him. "Do you think I've nothing better to do you fuckers, I've not come here to lose to a bunch of fucking monkeys." The effect on our team was devastatingly unnoticeable, not because we didn't think it was a disgraceful thing to say, but it was just that we were under the influence of an abusive parent that we were so scared of and not one of us was prepared to stand up to him in fear for our own safety. The effect on Cardiff College, however, was dramatic.

Their captain immediately called his players off the pitch and stood in the centre of a huddle.

This took several minutes, and we could not hear a single word that was said but even Gimson looked unnerved when they finally all turned as a unit and stared right at him. The ref pipped his whistle and both teams took their position for the second half. Within minutes, Cardiff were 1-0 ahead through a sweeping move down the left flank, a searching cross and a beautifully placed header by their captain, the lad that had wished me good luck. As Cardiff celebrated and returned to their positions their captain ran past Gimson who loudly, he didn't do quietly, shouted.

"What do you want, a fucking banana?"

The response was instant, brutal and one of the most beautiful things I had ever seen.

The Cardiff captain punched Gimson square on the nose, not a Hollywood punch, telegraphed and choreographed but with a control and symmetry of motion that led me to believe that football was not the only sport he excelled at. Gimson's legs immediately betrayed him, and his torso sought the sanctuary of the turf. Calmly, Cardiff College lined up for the restart. The Neath team stood silent, unmoving, unsure how to react. Surely Gimson would react and take out half their team with a burst of unfettered fury. We waited in a hushed silence. Then he slowly got to his feet with his nose hidden by both hands. He was crying, like a small child, blood streaming down his chin, disappearing into the camouflage of his shirt.

"He droke my dose", he exclaimed to the nearest Neath player, who turned away immediately. "He droke my bucking dose, " he repeated, shouting at the rest of the team.

We all refused eye contact and stood exactly still. "Are you all dowing to dand der and do dothing you wankers?" cried Gimson.

One Neath player broke ranks, walked slowly towards Gimson. It was Richard our captain, our true captain.

He didn't run or change his pace, he just walked till he was face to face with Gimson and said calmly, "Go on Jimmy, fuck off now, time you went."

Gimson flashed his eyes towards Richard and immediately, with total and utter submission turned and walked off the pitch and towards the changing rooms. Big Lou made a beeline for Gimson but was stopped in his Tonka tracks when Gimson shouted at him, "Fuck off Lou, you fucking midget."

"In for a penny," I thought.

Both teams were in total shock, but the referee took charge and returned the ball to centre spot for the restart. Richard shouted over to Big Lou, whose head was bobbing side to side in a manic fashion. "Bring Jeremiah on but get him to warm up first. Come on Neath, let's win this".

This instantly lifted Neath and we attacked immediately from the kick-off. I did as I was told and started to warm up along the touchline, darting back and fore and stretching my hamstrings as I excitedly prepared myself to enter the game. "Ready, Lou." I said, with the coolest voice as I could muster, trying to hide my nerves. Lou was not even looking at me. "Lou," I tried to engage, "I'm ready." "Just wait a bit," he replied in a higher pitch than usual. And so, I stood there for about five minutes. Eight minutes passed and I still hadn't gone on.

Neath had a corner after two long range shots.

"What are you playing at, Lou? Get Lyndon on, we are down to ten men," screamed Richard.

"Go on, Jeremiah," said Big Lou with an unhidden disgruntlement. I didn't need telling twice and ran onto the pitch, trying to cover the huge expanse to the other end of the pitch before the corner was taken. I was halfway between the centre spot and the edge of the area when the corner was taken and struggled to get there in time.

I put my head down and sprinted to make up the ground. Then I looked up to see where the ball was and saw that it was arcing long and over-hit towards the far corner of the box.

All the Neath attackers were marked tightly but I was on my own, unmarked.

Cardiff had not made any provision for me, and the ball sailed just high enough over all the heads of the players, both defenders and attackers.

It's then I realised the ball was falling perfectly for me, the right pace and height and would fall perfectly for my stride pattern. I hit the ball with a right footed volley. I knew, as soon as I hit it, that it was going in. The ball flew into the top of the netting with an unforgettable sound of rotating ball against cord. I had scored, six seconds after coming on, I had scored.

My teammates all had their backs to me and turned to see me standing there in complete shock with the widest smile on my face basking in the glory of vindication. The celebrations were frenzied and heartfelt. There was genuine relief and bewilderment that the game, which already seemed to have had many chapters, was now ours to win. I couldn't help myself in having a sneaky glance towards Big Lou. His moustache seemed to dance in anticipation of his managerial masterclass but there was no acknowledgement. For the rest of the game, Neath took charge and slowly started to control the game. Our captain was incredible as he organised and encouraged the very best out of the team. Cardiff was still a good team but lacked the ability of our players to create chances and keep possession.

This was the very first time I had really felt part of the team. I chased and committed to every challenge, even making a few intelligent passes into scoring positions. I had an overwhelming feeling this was my day, my match to win. I knew I would score the winner.

Everything ran right for me, the ball bounced at the right height, the passes I received all fell to my favoured right foot and my marker was weak on the ball and the type of journey man I dealt with every week with The Rovers. Three minutes left to play and after a barrage of shots and clearances their keeper fumbled the ball, and it spilled out to me on the edge of the six-yard box. There were two defenders on the line ready to give their lives to stop me blasting it into the net.

I feigned just that and cheekily side footed it under them both as they sprung off the ground to make themselves as big as possible.

Neath College won 2-1 against Cardiff College that day and I had scored both goals. We had reached the Welsh Colleges final and as far as football was concerned, it was the most satisfying and memorable day of my life.

I avoided Big Lou in the aftermath of the celebrations as I didn't want to give him the chance to "piss on my chips". We were victorious in the final against a college from Llanelli at the Welsh League ground of Briton Ferry. We won easily and again Big Lou found another ringer to prevent me from starting the match and, true to form, as we were ahead throughout the game, I never made an appearance.

Fuck you, Big Lou.

In the award ceremony at the end of the match, Big Lou gave me my winner's trophy, smiling gormlessly beneath his dad's tache, as I lined up last, behind my proud teammates. My trophy had a foot missing.

That semi-final match was indeed life changing, not because of the great day that it was or the headlines on the back page of the "Neath Guardian" that weekend, which read, "Jeremiah Saves Neath."

It was because of the handwritten letter I would receive the very next week.

I had never met my father and I had never really talked to my mam about him. She mentioned him occasionally, but never held him in a good light. She had told of his jealousy and his unreasonable behaviour but that was in conversation with others that I had overheard or when my presence had gone unnoticed. They had been together about a year after I was born, which was only a couple of months after they married, when they lived with his parents in a little village called Rhos, which was about eight miles from the one I had grown up in.

We had one remaining photograph of him, in the old piano stool in my Mam's bedroom. It had once been part of a larger photo of their wedding day but had been cut in half with acrimonious scissors sometime after they split. Sometimes when she was out, I used to open up the stool and find the picture and match it up with the corresponding half of my mother on that day. I always remember thinking that on his own he seemed mean-looking and intense. He was sitting down and looking up to the camera with, what looked like, a flash of anger in his eyes. When the two halves were reunited, when they were together on that day, his whole persona seemed to alter, and he looked surprised and part of a moment in time that was lost forever yet had meant something to them both. My Mother's joy in her half of the scene seemed to engulf his half and make him softer and more approachable.

That was many years before and I had not felt the need to seek out the picture after the age of about nine or ten. Several people used to enquire after him, in all innocence, that had known him, not realising what an open wound it had been when I was younger.

I knew he had been a decent footballer in his day and had an offer to be an apprentice at Swansea City but had been forced by his dad to take an apprenticeship with the Council, with more prospects. I knew he was a plumber but beyond that I knew nothing.

I had just started to venture into Neath on a Saturday night with my mate Charlie on the quest for beer and girls. The former was easily found which hampered dramatically the latter. One night, short of funds, we called in to see Charlie's dad, Bomber at "The Market Tavern." Charlie had said, "We'll wait till he's had a few then tap him up for a few quid, he'll be with his mates so will want to give it the big'un". I loved Bomber, he'd grown up with my mam as kids and was an intoxicating presence to be around. He was tall and dressed well.

The phrase "loveable rogue" seemed to have been invented for him. He had taken several vacations at Her Majesty's convenience for services to the reclaimed metal industry and whilst he was away my mam did Charlie's washing and made him the odd dinner with a special one on a Sunday. Charlie was right, Bomber was in the finest of moods that night and beckoned us from the other end of the busy pub.

"These are my boys," he exclaimed to his mates, immediately making me feel part of it all, as he always did. I swear that his comrades would not have looked out of place in a sixteenth century pirating pub in the Caribbean. They were the roughest collection of old sea dogs you could ever have imagined. There was not one with a full collection of body parts. Brian had a hand missing that had been left on a high voltage electricity cable one night whilst plundering the copper inside it. He wore a three-pronged hook which constantly held his wallet, daring any landlubber foolhardy enough to try to take it. Dai had an eye missing, which, if legend was to be believed, he could not remember losing and hadn't noticed it was gone till he woke up the next morning after a particularly heavy night. Tinker completed the crew. His only missing extremity was his thumb, which paled in cutlass-bearing comparison to the others, but seeing him do the, oh so predictable, disappearing thumb trick whilst chatting up a new young lady and her screaming at the realisation that it was actually missing was something I would never get tired of.

We stayed in their company for three free pints and had the most memorable of times hearing them regale their many adventures, none of which seemed either moral or legal.

Bomber sidled over to me at the bar. I leaned in, to compensate for the wonderful cacophony of the main bar, as he put his huge hand on my shoulder. "I saw your dad earlier, he was in 'The Duke,' if you're quick you might catch him," he said with a casualness that felt breathtakingly out of place. "Thanks Bomb," I just replied, before necking the last of my free plunder.

I nodded to Charlie, who was always a pint or two ahead of me and pointed for the door.

Minutes later, we were running towards "The Duke", stopping only to take a leak in the Pentecostal Church that lay exactly halfway between. As we stood against the great yew tree regifting our ballast, I said to Charlie, through the steam, "Do you think he'll be there Charl?"

"I fucking hope so boyo. About time you got this monkey off your back," he said with mild irritation. I glanced at him with a mix of bewilderment and anger. "And don't look at me like that, I know how much this messes with your head. You can't even mention him without getting emotional. Look, he'll be there, ok, and it will be like 'Little House on the fucking Prairie'. He might even buy us a few pints." With that he deliberately pushed me forward, causing me to headbutt the tree for balance whilst my two hands were occupied. I only just prevented getting piss on my trousers as I watched him run off, his laughter beckoning me to follow.

"The Duke" was rammed, with a heady mix of the underaged and the under-achieved. We could barely move forward let alone find my long-lost Father. I paused as the thought flashed across my mind. "What sort of bloke would drink in a shithole like this?"

Charlie, short of patience of any kind, gave a push forward causing the crowd in front of him to compress then sway to the left. This resulted in a few drinks being spilt and some empty glasses crash to the floor. There was now about ten feet between us as we were engulfed by the throng. I noticed a weaselly-looking bloke heading Charlie's way with a beer bottle in his hand. The bottle however was being held by the neck and there was no doubt what he was going to use it for.

I pushed forward and tried to head him off but there was no way I was going to make it in time as the crowd inconveniently parted and the back of Charlie's head looked like a watermelon that was just about to be split in two. I shouted a panicked warning, but Charlie could not hear. Weasel man raised his arm to get maximum downward force just close enough for me to snatch the bottle from his hand. As he still went through the motion, he turned to see me behind him with a glorious smile on my face. I completed my one upmanship with a cheeky wink. There then seemed to be a wave of movement in the crowd. As it convulsed to and fro, I felt someone's hand on my forehead then it was gone. I caught Charlie's eye and he indicated he would leave by the back door. I was closer to the front and would meet him outside.

To be engulfed in the cold night air was a blessed relief. I filled my lungs with the sweet smell of fish and chips and endless possibilities. The sweat from the incident inside dripped down my forehead and over my eyebrow, I wiped it with my hand but there was more than I'd realised, way more.

"Iesu Grist, Lynd, your face," Charlie appeared. I didn't know what he meant. I wiped the sweat again, this time I realised it was blood, blood pouring from a small wound above my right eye. The flow was encouraged by my increased temperature from our stint inside the bar. Quicker than a race day whippet, Charlie darted into the chip shop next door and came out with a swathe of serviettes and pressed them hard against the wound. "He sliced you, I saw him, with a piece of glass.

It was Terry Turd, what a bastard," seethed Charlie. "Let's get my dad, he hates the Turds." I didn't know who Charlie was talking about.

I knew of the Turds. Their actual name was Tudor, but this was Wales. A notorious family that seemed to be involved in everything that was bad about Neath. Every burglary, assault and breach of the peace seemed to be connected to one of them. "No, it's fine, let's head home, Charl," I said with a sad resignation. After the mad five minutes, it dawned on me that I wouldn't be meeting my father tonight, or any other night. It was a lost cause.

We started to walk the five miles home and very soon the blood dried on my cut, and we spent the rest of the journey making lists of the girls we would most like to have sex with. The list was as comprehensive as it was naively ambitious. We managed to flag a lift for the second half of the distance home with Dai Roundabout, who twenty years earlier had had the slight misfortune to crash his car on the way home from the pub on a roundabout. From that night on any surname, he or any his family had used was banished forever and the legend was born. I waved goodnight to Charlie and Dai and walked the remaining minutes home, weighing up the pros and cons of finishing the night with either toasted crusts with jam or masturbation.

I decided on both. It had been an extremely stressful night.

The next morning, my injury was easily explained to my wonderfully gullible Mother. I had become so used to her believing everything I said that my excuses had become so outlandish that they were often worse than the secret I was attempting to cover up.

She sat opposite me at the kitchen table and, out of character for her, looked me straight into my eyes and handed me an envelope folded neatly in half, betraying the fact it had been kept nervously in her pinny for days.

"This came, I think it's from your father," she never used the word Dad, not even to describe her own. It was small, neat and was written in the most beautiful handwriting. It was addressed to my mother. Before I knew it, it was opened, unfolded and the single sheet was in my hands ready to read. There was no nervousness or hesitancy, just a random period of solitude, quietness, and peace. Mam got up and left the table, leaving me imprisoned in the silence.

The letter was short and to the point. It read...

Dear Ange,

I am sorry I have not been in contact. My mother is very ill and would like to meet Lyndon before she passes. Can you ask him if he would get in touch, please? My phone number is below.

Love

Albert

P.S. I am very sorry.

His telephone number and address were at the bottom of the page. I handed it to my Mam who said, "I don't bloody want it," took it, read it, rolled her eyes, and returned it. For days, I thought about that letter. Late night walks around the village under the faltering streetlamps brought no resolution but became longer each evening. Every thought imaginable coursed through my mind.

Excitement, resentment, and repulsion all competed for dominance but, as soon as one was beaten to within an inch of its life, it got up and battled on, bloodied yet indestructible. The next evening, I carefully removed the letter from under my mattress and headed to the phone box with my carefully gathered coins that I kept in an old black container used to hold camera films. It had a grey lid. I had always wondered why it did, but it was never resolved.

The coins rattled the theme tune to "Grange Hill" in my pocket as I ran the short distance only to find Vaughn Thomas in occupation, noisily cajoling his fancy woman that only half the village knew about. He looked over his shoulder to find that he was being watched and ended the call abruptly. He left the box with a glance of the guilty but nodded anyway, crippled with an innate shy politeness. I prepared for my mission on the shelf next to the phone. I laid out my coins in a line in tens, fives, and twos. I took out the letter, even though I had memorised the number within minutes of its receipt. I slid the edge of the letter into the corner of the chrome frame on the back wall that contained long lost information that was now obscured by names scratched in the Perspex, mine being one of them.

I was ready. I dialled the number, then waited.

Beep, beep, beep.

I pressed in two ten pence coins and waited again. I had heard he was remarried and waited for a female voice to answer. "Hello," said a man's voice. I was not expecting that, and an agonising silence ensued.

"Hello, it's Lyndon," I eventually mustered in my best parlour voice.

"Hello, Son," said my father, with a calmness that had the opposite effect on me. "Cheeky fucker" I thought. "How could he go straight in at son? Fucking son? Where were you all these years, you bastard?"

"You wanted to meet?" I said, belying my incandescence. "Tomorrow, I'll pick you up," said the man with the blurry face and ever-changing proportions. What do I do now? Shit, I wished I had not called. I thought about hanging up.

The nine o'clock bus rumbled past, giving me time to think. "No, pick me up at Pen-a-wern corner tomorrow at three, the game is off." Why did I say that? Stupid thing to say, bollocks.

"OK, how is the football going?" I hung up. Ten pence vomited into the unused coin slot, and I collected it immediately, adding it to the coins already in the camera film tube. My head itched. I scratched it with both hands, clawing at my scalp in awkward irritation.

I knew this to be a sign of frustration, anger even. I wished I had not rung him. I left the phone box and walked home deep in thought. Vaughn Thomas lurked behind the itchy bush at Mrs Prothero's, ready to continue his clandestine pacification of the short-skirted and morally devoid.

I lay in bed late the next morning, late for me. The morning replaced the gloom of the previous evening with a neatly wrapped gift of optimism. I tore open its brightly coloured wrappings and drenched myself in its contents. I contemplated who I should be that day. I decided I would show him what he had missed out on.

I would be aloof, measured, relaxed and superior even though I was none of those.

I would be taller, stronger, and more intelligent with a glorious future and no requirement for an insignificant father. I would show him I could look after my mother and give her the protection he never contemplated. I would appear briefly, fleetingly in his life, draw him in. I would make him love me, make his heart burst with pride, then at the last minute leave his life with a bitter coldness that would haunt him for the rest of his empty days. Well, that was the plan.

I stood at Pen-a-wern corner for five minutes to three. I wanted to be late, but I had never been able to be anything but punctual in my life, up to that point and to this day. I soon realised this was not a trait I had inherited from him. At a quarter past three I stood there analysing the various cars that passed, even approaching the kerb on two occasions when cars slowed to take the corner only to awkwardly exchange glances with an old lady and a fat bloke delivering oil.

What eventually pulled up beside me was beyond even my worst imaginings.

I was about to leave, I'd done my bit, no harm done. The green Austin Maxi mounted the kerb unceremoniously and lurched to a stop, stalling in the process. The passenger door was pushed open from inside and immediately closed on itself because of the weight of its overengineered mass and the fact that the wheels were higher up on that side. I opened the door and looked inside. Before I could get my bearings or greet my father with my overprepared opening statement he said, "Get in boy." And there it was. The first words from my long-lost father.

"Get-in-boy."

Like I had robbed a post office and the getaway driver was seventeen minutes late. Like I was an afternoon rent boy, plying his trade to a passing John or the last evacuee left at the railway station. I was lost for words and the whole situation was not in my control. I bristled, nearly told him to "fuck off," nearly slammed the door in his face and walked away like a western.

Nearly, but not. I held the door and tried to get in but there was a problem, a significant one at that. The Maxi had no passenger seat. No seat at all, just a blue, metal concertina toolbox with a handle pointing vertically upwards, where the seat should have been.

 Was I missing something? Was this normal? He did not seem to be aware that this was anything but normal. What should I say? Do I make a point? What was I supposed to do? I did the only thing that I could do. I folded the handle flat, sat on the toolbox and pretended this was a perfectly acceptable mode of transportation.

Jimmy Saville's voice in my head reassuringly reminded me of "Clunk Click, every trip," but frankly it didn't seem worthwhile.

If we were to have a hideous crash, then the seatbelt would only hold me in place as various plumbing tools embedded themselves in my rectum. If that was bad, the restarting of the engine was hell itself. Three times the key turned to no avail.

I was convinced there was no engine in there at all, more tools or an old copper boiler with a sick pig trapped inside. I looked at the man next to me for the first time. He was small, partly because of my elevated position but also because of his slight frame.

He was handsome in an angry way though this could have been because of his tortured embarrassment of the car not starting.

He was athletic and fit looking. His hair was as black as mine and styled in the same way as the photo from seventeen years earlier. He closed his eyes and turned the key again. For the first time, I felt his anguish, his embarrassment. I rooted for him. I longed for him to start the engine, not for me, not to end this vacuous moment that was sucking our lives away, but to end his turmoil and make some positive first impression that he must have longed for. The pig made an instant recovery and the engine burst into life, an explosion from the exhaust pipe and cloud of grey smoke announced we were back in the game. He turned to me and smiled, there was relief in his face with a smattering of humour. I took the smile, enlarged it, and gave it back immediately, with a light dusting of nervous laughter. We were off.

Within minutes, I could feel his anxiety, like a vine growing throughout the car, creeping slowly in my direction. "Time to put him out of his misery," I thought. "How is work?" I said with a strange gaiety that I instantly regretted. "Err, yeah, good. Work is good. I am a plumber," he said quietly. "Yeah, I know," I responded quickly then wondered if it sounded aggressive, which it was not meant to. "Course you do, I mean good... good," he croaked, I saw a glimmer of self-doubt and immediately recognised our mutual foe.

"Umm, I thought we would go and see my mam and dad, they've been looking forward to it, it's not far," he said, less frog-like.

I knew how far it was, I knew where they lived, what village anyway. For seventeen years I had been working on this jigsaw. Where my grandparents lived was one of the few pieces I had to endlessly take apart and put back together, never progressing, never forming a picture, never being able to put the box away. "Fine, that's fine," I said, more relieved than anything. Honestly, if he had said we were stopping off to meet the execution committee for the Third Reich then I would have been relieved. Anything to terminate this endless awkwardness that was only minutes old. The rest of the journey was in silence, broken only by the squeak of the toolbox beneath the gentle undulation of my comatosed backside.

We pulled up outside a very pretty, well kept, semi-detached, ex council house. The garden was painstakingly manicured, the rendered finish was painted in colours of warmth and safety and glowed like a place where time passes slowly. I felt a huge contrast with the house I had left that morning. A house of constantly changing uncertainty, full of love yet with the constant undertone of sporadic violence. We got out of the car and blood rushed to my already shaky legs. I blamed it on the toolbox, but I knew I was nervous. I was not the only one. My father, avoiding eye contact, led the way through the wrought iron gate and up the pixie path to the front door. He went straight in, leaving me outside. I sensed an opportunity to run that I was never going to take. I paused and congratulated myself in commiseration that life would never be the same again. It never was.

I entered the hallway. Empty. No sound. No welcoming committee.

Were they too old to leave their front room? Were they in bed there like the grandparents of Charlie Bucket, one at either end?

I continued down the hall. "Hello," I said. No answer.

I passed the best room. All set out for nobody. Awkward seats surrounded a kidney-shaped occasional table with black, spindly legs with gold tips. I saw the kitchen ahead of me. The kettle boiled excitedly on the flame, moments from glory. There was only one room left downstairs, the door, mostly shut, had a brown, curved, Bakelite handle.

I held it, took a deep breath, and entered. I tried to keep control, to process the moment but it was completely impossible. The room was full of people, there could have been six or thirty-six, I could not tell. The noise went from silence to full euphoria the moment I entered.

There were high pitched squeals, hands put to faces in wondrous delight. Shovel-sized hands slapped on my back, then slid up to my neck and squeezed before going further north and ruffling my hair. My hands were held and caressed, my face was lovingly touched, and I was spun around from one familiar stranger to another. I was kissed, hugged, patted and cwtched.

The kettle screamed in celebration, begging to be let in to join the party. There were voices that felt like I had heard them a thousand times but never at all. There were smells I thought I knew, all wrapped in a warmth that would last a dozen lifetimes. It is only in beautiful nostalgia that I can recount the moment with any sort of correlation.

There was my Aunty Jocelyn, my father's sister who, little did I know then, had counted down the minutes till she saw me again after having me so cruelly ripped from her life. She wept and danced and smelt me so very deeply and unashamedly as if to somehow replenish the years of missed love.

There was also my Uncle Terry, Joce's husband. Together they were two halves of the same person. A huge bear of a man, with an inexhaustible laugh and barrel-chested bravado. His smile lit every part of every room he was in, and he would go on to tell me tales of such wild exaggeration and outlandish tomfoolery that it is one of the reasons I have tears in my eyes, tapping at this keyboard today.

There were cousins, second cousins, aunties and uncles of all descriptions, great uncles, greater aunties, too many to count, too many to remember, too many to hug, to kiss, to answer their many questions. Then the room quietened, not to a hush, more of an air of expectation. People moved away, just gently. I realised something of importance was about to happen. I turned to see an old man get out of his seat, slowly at first but with strength and composure. I knew it was my grandfather, Ellis, it had to be. He stood in front of his armchair. He was shorter than me but broad with a smile to match.

He had his hair combed over to one side with large hornbeam, rounded glasses. He was wearing a suit with his tie in a Windsor knot. A large walnut burr pipe was removed from his mouth as a large cloud of smoke announced his arrival into my life.

"Lyndon, my boy, come on," his arms outstretched in front of him.

It was impossible to resist, even if I'd had such a ridiculous notion. His embrace was strong, manly, and soft. It was the first time I took into my lungs the aroma of pipe tobacco and Brut 33. A heady mix of lovely devilment and loyalty at all costs. Years of non-male contact drained away as every bone in my body turned to playdough. It was as addictive as any drug I had never taken.

Then, like a golden prize, I was straightened, repositioned, and presented to what everyone in the room, except me, knew was the main event. I hadn't noticed her at all, which was understandable. In her armchair sat my grandmother, Janet.

She was quite possibly the smallest and thinnest woman I had ever seen. She looked light as a sparrow as she tried furiously to get the last possible puff out of her cigarette. After extinguishing her current and constant companion, she tried her level best to compose herself. She was shaking in glorious anticipation as, with both hands free, she trembled from the shoulders down. An overwhelming smile came from every pore of her face as she looked up at me from her seated position. Not expecting her to get up, I kneeled in front of her.

I was on solid ground now. I knew old ladies; my life had been full of them.

Hard ones, soft ones. Ones with glorious depths of love and those with a tendency to strike out at the slightest provocation. I had been on the backfoot all afternoon in the company of such man love, but this was my speciality, making old ladies happy.

I was aware that the whole room was watching as I held my grandmother's hands in mine. "It's so lovely to meet you. I'm Lyndon," I said quietly. "Oh, Lyndon bach, mae fy machgen adref, Oh Lyndon bach, dod yma," she said.

My Welsh was good enough to know how much I meant to her as we embraced, dislodging her glasses, and mixing her tears with mine. I sat with her for ages as she laughed and stroked my face and hands. It was lovely, perfectly lovely, lovely in the best possible description of lovely and by the time everyone had left it was just my Nan and Gags and Uncle Terry left. By this time, I felt like I had known them all for an eternity. Black and white photos of a baby that looked just like me, were strewn across the floor with people I would never get to meet. My Mamgu and Tadcu, my father's grandparents, held me so very proudly, not knowing it was the last time they would touch my skin or smell my baby hair. My emotional bucket was full.

I made a toilet excuse, just to get some air, and caught the tail end of a severe chastisement by my auntie Joce aimed at my father who was trapped on a stool in the kitchen like a cuckolded schoolboy in the naughty corner. Her mood changed instantly upon seeing me and she cupped my face in her hands and said,

"My handsome boy. Rwy'n dy garu di," and held my face and kissed my cheek with the delicacy of a second row forward, then swept out of the room with no remnant of the anger she had shown moments before. Alone for the first time in several hours I looked at my father. I think the full force of the moment had hit him. How the effect of his actions had affected so many people and what they had all missed.

For the second time that day I felt an empathy for him, a thoroughly undeserved courtesy that was only offered because of the wondrous day I had had.

I was strong now, in charge. Confident in the role I had built for myself to combat those that had everything to hide how little I had. That day's events had changed everything. I was king of the world.

"I think we need a drink," I announced to my father, round shouldered, and dishevelled. His eyes darted to mine. I will never forget the appreciation in his face at the chance of escaping the hell he must have gone through in that last couple of hours. "A splendid idea," he rejoiced. With the speed of a shoplifting squirrel, he gathered his fags and lighter and said a quick goodbye to all and said he'd meet me in the car.

My departure was a little more drawn out with more kisses, cwtches and promises to come back tomorrow for my Sunday dinner.

In contrast to earlier, the snaffling pig grunted in appreciation as we pulled away from my grandparent's house.

My waving endurance was tested to near breaking point as the house was still visible from a hundred yards away and my new family saw no signs of tiring as we finally turned the corner out of sight. The conversation this time was easier, full of glowing appreciation of the people I had just met.

For the first time there was a shared experience, short though it had been. I became aware that I was talking too much but it was hard not to. He didn't seem to mind.

He preferred it, I thought. I was animated and poetic and probably a little irritating.

It must have been a longer journey than I'd realised as we pulled up at a pub. "The Eagle's Bush" was of legendary status, for no good reason whatsoever.

It was in the middle of Briton Ferry, an extension of Neath. I had only ventured there on a few occasions to play football and once to a particularly violent party, where Charlie had broken a lad's nose with a copy of "The Yellow Pages." We were being chased up the stairs by some local gate crashers and in his attempt to slow them down he grabbed the first item to hand.

He threw it like a boomerang, spine first and the solid yellow missile hit the first fella square on the bridge of his conk. The sound was gut wrenching, like a stick broken over your knee. The whole crew tumbled like a game of downhill skittles. After dive bombing them off the top step and landing several farewell punches, we stayed, and they made their forced apologies and left.

I looked over at the old clock at the Metal Box factory, it had stopped at five minutes to eleven. Some had said it stopped at precisely the moment Barry John retired from Welsh rugby.

As we entered through the front door, I realised my father may have been in "The Duke" that night. Shitholes were his preferred environment.

The familiar smell of stale beer, fags and broken promises flooded my senses as we entered the bar.

"Albert," came the shout in unison from a variety of species I was unfamiliar with. I glanced around the room.

There seemed twenty pairs of eyes holding me in their glare as I quickly knitted together their life stories in my mind.

Sat at the bar were the Scratcher, the Shaker, the Fat Troublemaker. Talking secretly in the corner was Tweedle Scum and Tweedle Flea. Across the rest of the bar, I could make out Screw, Glue, Ain't-got-a-clue, Fagbutt, Dribble and Slug.

"Hello Albert, the usual?" said the less than hygienic barkeeper, "Who is this Twat?" I bristled immediately and turned crimson. I looked at my father who smiled gently and looked up from sorting the coins in his hand and said, matter-of-factly, "This is my boy, Lyndon, and if you call him that again, I'll rip you a new arsehole." "Yayyyy," came the shout from the cast of "One flew over the Cuckoo's Nest." The landlord laughed a deep throaty laugh and said, "Welcome Lyndon, we've all heard a lot about you. I'm Dick." and reached over the bar and offered a handshake.

I took his hand and spluttered a smile in tortured relief. "So, you're Sticky Dicky," I thought, impressed to be in the company of a leading member of the Neath Tafia. "Welcome," "Croeso", "Good boy, Lyndon," rang the varied greetings from around the bar. I turned to my father who was loving the moment, I pushed him at the shoulder. He, in return, patted and squeezed mine. I felt at ease with the banter, I spoke fluent banter.

"What can I get you, son?" said my father. "Son," suddenly seemed more acceptable. I paused, theatrically considered the various pumps on the bar, then announced.

"Well, there's seventeen years of fucking pocket money for a start."

"Yay hey!!" came the shout from the greatest bar collective in the world. "You've met your match there, Albert," said one. "He's your boy alright, Jerry," said another. "I'll have a lager," I said with a wink.

Then we got drunk, well I got drunk, noticeably drunk, in a short space of time. The pints appeared and I drank them. I lost count at five but there were many more. The evening was a riot with stories and tales about my father and his band of miscreants. There were songs and arguments with even a few unlanded punches thrown in fond debauchery, signalling the end of the night for the culprit who was lovingly poured into a taxi and sent packing, off home to wear his dinner.

In a lull at the end of the evening, my father and I sat down in the corner. The room spun like a night on the Waltzers, but I'd slowed my intake as the pints had become less frequent, which I was very thankful for. "I read about you in 'The Neath Guardian.' You scored two goals in the semi-final, well done boy", he leaned in. I was pleased to get the compliment, but I had already worked out that the write up in the local paper was probably the reason we were sitting there that evening, not my grandmother's health, which in my untrained medical opinion seemed fine. The fact that she was to live for another eight years seems to back this up.

Then he said something that did have a much greater effect on me. "I came to see you in the final, at Briton Ferry. It is a shame that little bastard did not put you on." "What? you came to see me, in the final?" I gulped, suddenly overcome with drunken surprise.

"I wanted to come up to you, I asked which one you were, but I knew straight away, you look like your Mam. It was a shitty move by Bridget not to put you on, even when you were three goals up."

I gathered my inebriated emotions, but I was confused. "Who, the fuck, is Bridget?" I slurred. "Bridget the Midget.

Big Lou, you called him. I used to play football with him years ago for Cilfrew Rovers. Horrible little ferret he was and one footed with it, that was another of his nicknames, 'The one footed wonder,' he could not pass a plum stone. I suppose, looking back, we made his life a misery. We left him in the shitter at the "The Miners Arms" in Pontrhydyfen once, on the way back from a game, his Mam had to fetch him on her moped." Suddenly, it all made sense. That is why I had had to put up with all the shit from Lou. The constant criticism, the jibes, and the difficult fight to make the team. I sat for a while, levelling it all up in my head. I felt, at that moment, that this may be the first of many revelations I would discover about the man sitting next to me. I decided I did not give a shit. I grinned a drunken grin.

"To Big Lou," I toasted. "Bridget the Midget," my father regaled. We laughed without a care and drained our glasses. "Time to go," he said. "It is not far, we'll leave the car and pick up a Chinese on the way, I bet you are starving." "I could eat a scabby horse," I agreed in a long, drawn-out sentence with no discernible gaps between the words. It was a bright evening and the glow from the steelworks in Port Talbot crept slowly upwards in a half-arsed attempt to kidnap the moon. It was only a couple of hundred yards before we reached the Chinese takeaway. It was like a million others found in towns all over Wales, complete with garish reds and golds, waving cats and translucent waterfalls in the window.

"I've got someone I'd like you to meet," my father over pronounced, the night air getting the better of him too as we entered "The Dragon." The bell above the door tinkled our arrival. It was empty inside and the counter was unmanned. We waited a while until a very striking Chinese teenage girl appeared. "Hello Albret," she said delightedly. "How are you? You not been in for long time." I corrected her grammar in my head but took it no further. She really was beautiful.

Her shoulder length hair was raven black and she smiled with her eyes. She dressed in a traditional Chinese dress which glimmered in gold and jade.

"Lyndon, this is Jai Li, it means good and beautiful." They shared a smiling glance of a lost, shared conversation. "Jai, this is my son, Lyndon, you will get to know him, he'll be around from now on."

"Hello, Ryndon," she said, looking up shyly through her perfectly straight, fringed hair. "Hello, Jai, um Jai Li, sorry, pleased to meet you," I said in my best sober voice. She blushed ever so slightly. "The usual Albret, but for two?" "Yes, please my darling," said my father with genuine affection. She disappeared behind the slatted curtain, and we sat in the corner and waited for our food. The familiar aromas of the East flirted with my tantalised taste buds. I really was hungry, and I knew I would feel less lightheaded with some food inside me. I tried not to succumb to the almost instant feelings of tiredness as I sat on the leatherette chair in the corner.

It was not long before the bell above the door tinkled again as new customers arrived. Two enormous men entered with mis-matched beer guts and ill-fitting tee shirts.

Bearded and the worse for drink, they rested their considerable bulk against the mahogany panelled counter. Jai Li entered and immediately disappeared again. Moments later she re-appeared and said very animatedly. "You must leave, I will not serve you this time. You are not welcome here. You must go now." "Come on Suzy Wong, keep your knickers on. We only want a bloody Chinky," said the greasy one with the "Iron Maiden" Tee shirt on. "Oh preeze, Jonny will ruv you rong time," chipped in the sweaty one with a nose ring. "Wankers," I thought. Then I became instantly aware that my father was visibly starting to twitch. He had started to roll his shoulders and his head was moving to the side in, what seemed to be, an involuntary motion.

His hands were extending and clenching in unison. Before I could comprehend the situation, my father stood up and moved to the centre of the room. His twitching had stopped, and he stood there completely still. My awareness had been heightened and for the first time that day I noticed that he was, almost completely, dressed in black. At five foot three inches, my father's black leather box jacket covered his black shirt which was opened lower than was currently fashionable. This was finished off by a chain, displaying, what, I had been told by my Auntie Joce, were the buttons from my first baby booties. His black drainpipe trousers were razor sharp as they almost reached his black, slip on shoes. The only member of the ensemble that had not got the colour memo were his polar white sport socks. He slowly took out a black comb from his trouser back pocket and casually ran it through his black Brylcreemed hair, peppered with grey but only at the temples. Greasy and Sweaty were unaware of his presence until, mid comb, my father said, "You heard the lady; you are not welcome here. It's time to fuck off, boys." A small micro twitch in my father's neck betrayed the intensity of the moment. Greasy turned first with the speed of a sloth on his day off to see my father. He blinked his eyes to try to formulate an explanation of what was before him. It refused to register. Greasy nudged Sweaty and he turned like the first sloth's slower cousin but with one eye shut from the weight of the booze. I had been in some scrapes before, but this was momentous. I saw no other outcome of this glorious day than to be beaten shitless by the two silverbacks blocking our escape route. Sweaty had also struggled to assess the situation, especially through one eye as he staggered to keep his beer balance. He theatrically looked my father up and down and eventually said, "Fuck me, it's Zorro."

The moment was excruciating. I was unable to see any way out other than total obliteration. Then, in an unexpected turn, the two of them fell into each other's arms in an explosion of laughter, grabbing on tightly in a stooped position. They held their genitals to stop from pissing themselves. They convulsed in breathless laughter until, eventually, they could only wipe the tears from their eyes. My father's twitch returned. "Come on Gaz, let's try the "China Garden", it's on the way home," said Greasy. "Good one Baz," said Sweaty, and with that they disappeared through the tinkle. Their laughter could be heard for what seemed an eternity as the room returned to a deathly quiet. The silence spread like a wildfire until my father turned to me with, what I expected to be, a solemn embarrassment but was masquerading as a huge smile. He too burst into laughter and ran over and gave me a huge cwtch, then said. "Bloody hell, son, I thought we were dead meat then. Did you see the fucking size of them?" I was truly wrapped up in the whole euphoria of the moment and felt honoured that my father was prepared to share his beating with me. We hugged and spun around and laughed with all our newfound energy. "Thank you, Albret," said Jai Li, clapping her hands with delight. "Thank you, little Albret," she ran round from the counter and threw herself into my arms and kissed me full on the lips. It was one of many memorable kisses that day, though it may have been my favourite. We took our bagged-up food from the counter and re-joined the night sky.

It welcomed us like the final curtain of the opening night of a sure-fire hit at the Swansea Grand Theatre. "It's been a good day," I said, hoping to steal the applause. I looked at my father. The photograph in the piano stool in my Mam's bedroom seemed impossible to visualise now.

"Come on, son of Zorro, let's go home," laughed my Dad.

A Star-Spangled Manner

Friendship is a strange concept, these days more than in the past. I've heard my daughters say the exact number of friends they have, only to find out that they are also known as followers depending on which social media platform they are referring to. Their real friends are also their Facebook friends but then there are an army of people that they have never met that are also emptied into the hopper marked "friend." I suppose I am guilty as anyone in falling into this regimented way of collecting friends in alphabetical order on my life support system that, until a few years ago, I had no idea I required. Minor successes with poems I've posted online and some children's books I've self-published has meant that my "friends" on Facebook have grown larger than people I have shared experiences with to people that I have never met who have a preconceived notion of who I am and what my thoughts on various subjects are. All of this is rather splendid, and I have had some perfectly lovely conversations online with people from across the globe that I would never have had the opportunity to meet or converse with otherwise. I am also incredibly grateful for the additional book sales that the internet has produced. The best part of this computerised connection with the rest of the planet, for me, has been being able to rekindle connections from years past that I otherwise would have been unable to do.

One lazy afternoon, I had been looking on the website of Camp Shohola in Pennsylvania USA. I had spent a glorious summer there in 1986 and I was curious to know if the place was how I had remembered it. After scrolling through the rather archaic website, I decided it was exactly as it had been and after several minutes of reminiscing, I sighed deeply and closed my laptop, wondering if my children realised I had once been young too, and wasn't just the old fella who never refused a taxi call out and embarrassed them sometimes at family get togethers.

Several days later, my account was brought to the attention of Mark Zuckerberg, CEO of Facebook, killer of conversations, destroyer of dreams and the person solely responsible for the fact that two of my children have never read a novel, one refused to eat an apple off a tree and another thought that Cameron Diaz was once the Prime Minister of Great Britain. After a short deliberation and, no doubt, a maniacal laugh, he immediately ordered my demise by sending out his most ruthless agents to mess with my gentle, unexceptional life.

On Facebook, in the section that nobody ever takes notice of called "People you may know," one day popped up the name of someone I recognised. Her face, though obviously older, was as pretty as I had remembered. Memories of our first kiss and that wonderful summer came flooding back. I guiltily clicked on her profile and found genuine pleasure in the pictures of her with her family and the adventures they had over several holidays, or vacations, as they would have surely referred to them. Gabrielle had been my holiday romance that summer in 1986 and our different nationalities and cultural nuances had made the whole experience more exciting and memorable for both of us.

Great days, I thought, returning to the present with only minor thoughts of what might have been. The very next day I had a friend request from Gabrielle, out of the blue. "What demonical algorithm is this?" I thought, cynically dismissing both fate and coincidence.

On one hand, I was delighted to catch up with an old friend. On the other, I was not stupid enough not to realise that something that starts so innocently can escalate into hurt and deception at the drop of a baseball cap.

After a short and unconvincing period of deliberation, due to the safety of both of our married relationships and indeed the distance between us negated any potential physical faux pas, I decided, "What the hell, it will be nice to catch up."

I accepted her friend request.

Within a matter of hours, due, I guess, to the time differences between the lands of "Hope and Glory" and "The Free", I had a direct message from Gabrielle and very quickly this developed into a wonderful text conversation. We talked about our partners and our careers, our children and most readily about our unbelievable memories of that one summer in '86.

When we were approaching what I thought was the beginning of the end of the conversation Gabrielle said, "There is a reason I have contacted you after all these years." I did not panic, ours had been a very innocent relationship and was everything that was good about having a summer romance.

"This sounds ominous," I replied.

"I've been dying to tell you for so many years, but we lost touch after a couple of letters," she continued, "I went to college, and I think you did too." "I did, and you will know how distracting that can be. I thought it might have been my fault that you stopped writing." I added with a tinge of regret. "It was, Lyndon, those photographs you took had very serious consequences indeed," she said, in what read like, a very serious tone for the first time. "Photographs, what photographs?" I said, genuinely not knowing what she meant.

When Gabrielle started to remind me, suddenly, every single detail of that summer came flooding back...

At the start of that summer of '86 I had watched the post for days, hoping that I would hear from them soon. I had seen an advert on the back of a magazine on sport science in the library at Neath Tertiary College. I don't know why I was reading that particular journal; my level of sport science was helping Old Tommy mark out the pitch on a Saturday morning and using a bit of orange string and a peg in the ground at one end and a handful of sawdust at the other to mark the centre circle.

The advert had been for "soccer counsellors" to work in The United States through a scheme called "Camp America." This was beyond my wildest dreams; nobody I knew had been to America. At first, I dismissed it as ridiculous. Boys like me didn't travel to America and speak to real Americans and eat hotdogs and say, "Howdy Ma'am." Everyone I knew echoed this, who dismissed the idea as "apple pie in the sky." But I sent the application form off and within days got a reply inviting me for an interview at Swansea University.

I went, spoke to a nice, posh chap from England and decided on the way home that if I got the chance to go it would be life changing. If not, then bollocks to it.

This mantra of mine had got me this far in life, I had nothing to lose.

That morning was to be very memorable. Those moments in life, as I opened that letter to say I had been accepted, are like little diamonds in time. Sometimes you think that they will never appear but when they do all you can do is to enjoy their sparkle. Do not count on them, they will never appear. Do not envy those that are presented with diamonds on a silk cushion week after week with little effort from themselves because their magnificence will go unnoticed.

Enjoy your diamonds. This one was mine and I still find warmth from its glow.

Over the next few weeks, I told everyone that would listen to me about my upcoming adventure until it got to the point where people were avoiding me. Even Billy Bullshit, the village bore who, daily, stole precious time from unsuspecting villagers that they would never see again, started to give me a wide berth.

On the morning of my departure, I went to see my friend Bethan as this was her wedding day and, because of my early National Express bus to Heathrow, I would miss the ceremony. We had been the best of friends and next-door neighbours since infants' school and the house was full of the anticipation of the big day with Nanas and Aunties clapping excitedly and eyeing the teapot like they were trying to give up the booze.

"Go up Lynd, she's having a moment," said Aunty Alice in almost complete submission. The stairs were strewn with all things matrimonial, and the house seemed smaller to me at that moment.

I found Bethan in her bedroom deeply lost in the mirror. She looked beautiful in her wedding dress and her hair in ringlets, and it was the first time I had seen her in makeup.

She turned and stood when she saw me. She smiled and I could just about make out her baby bump above the satin braiding as the dress flared out to the chiffon swathes of fabric.

"You look stunning," I said, meaning every word, "I haven't got long."

"A big day for us both," said Bethan with the start of a tear in her eye. "Don't say any more, just make sure you have an adventure big enough for both of us."

I tried to walk closer to give her a cwtch, but she stopped me.

"You'll make me cry and spoil my makeup," she whispered, dabbing her eyes with a hankie.

So, I left. Left her to her special day. Left her to the years of drabness, the evenings of waiting and worry, the endless tedium, and self-induced daydreams to escape her never-changing life of pleasing another who was so undeserving of her love.

I did not see her again, until many years later. We were only memories to each other by then.

Our childhoods had been parcelled away whilst the difficulties of life were wrestled into submission. We have become strangers now, though I think of her often.

Heathrow was an incredible culture shock for me. I had never seen so many people and soon realised it was unnecessary to say hello to everyone as they insected their way to where they needed to be. I had never flown before or really been out of Wales more than a weekend in Blackpool and a day trip to Weston-Super-Mare. It was so exciting as I slowly broke the code of the signage system and deciphered the announcements over the tannoy.

Camp America had chartered a huge Boeing 747, it said it on the side of the plane. I was part of a swarm mentality of excitement as we all tried to get our rucksacks and other bizarrely shaped luggage into the overhead compartments and took our seats. Everyone on the flight was leaving Britain for their American Summer Camp experience so a couple of movies were shown, en masse to the entire plane.

As I settled into "The Breakfast Club", I got chatting to a lovely girl called Sue from Surrey who sat next to me. She was clever and witty and the five and half hour flight passed like a flash as our friendship seemed unbreakable by the time the wheels touched down at JFK Airport in New York. Sue was giggling as we stood up to get our luggage, about a story or two I had told her in my newfound, valley-boy confidence. As she walked ahead of me, I immediately noticed a large patch of blood on the bottom of Sue's white, cheesecloth dress.

"Sue, you've hurt yourself," I said loudly, "I think your bottom is bleeding." Sue swivelled and looked at the rear of her dress. She shut her eyes for a moment and seemed to go white.

I'd seen that look before when I'd pretended to find a severed finger in a Swan Vestas box which was in fact my own finger poked through the bottom, laid on cotton wool and covered in ketchup and showed it to Mrs French in the village shop.

I immediately took this as a sign that Sue was going to faint and so I instantly took charge of the situation.

"Can we have some assistance please, can we have some help, PLEASE!" I shouted to try and alert the cabin crew.

"My friend is injured. She is bleeding," I continued, "She is BLEEDING."

Sue was not looking well at all as she tried to stop me from making a fuss. "Please stop," she whispered, "Please, please stop."

My plan was having an effect, most of the people on the plane were now aware of Sue's injury and started to move away from her to give her space. Some must have disliked blood as they grimaced at Sue, who had her head in her hands. There was still no clear way for the hostess to get through, so I intensified my assistance, louder this time.

"Can we please have some assistance, PLEASE, my friend has injured her BOTTOM."

Sue, took her hands off her face and screamed,

"WILL YOU JUST SHUT THE FUCK UP, YOU WELSH PRICK."

"She's gone into shock," I thought. The Hostess arrived and Sue was helped away to the safety of the first aid box. "Good luck, Sue," I shouted, forgiving her for her earlier outburst, "Have a lovely summer."

I was close to the front exit of the plane now. There was a guy a couple of years older than me who was enjoying the flight as much as I had been.

"Mate, you are a fucking legend," he said, laughing his congratulations in a deep cockney accent. "Just did what anyone else would have done," I said, rather proud of myself. "Not everyone would have done that, mate," his congratulations continued as I left the plane.

Customs took forever but eventually I found myself in the underground bus station of the Airport, aboard one of the famous Greyhound buses bound for Camp Shohola. As the bus reached the top of the ramp, I waited for the summer sun of the USA to burst through the windows in a star-spangled manner but was disappointed to find it very grey and muggy. The outside must have been pretty cold too as the temperature plummeted inside the vehicle in total contrast to the heat of the subterranean bus depot. It was only when we reached our first rest stop two hours later that I realised it had been my introduction to tinted windows and air conditioning.

At the roadside stop, I had my first experience of real America. The weather was sweltering, and the land was completely flat as far as the eye could see. Names I had heard of and names I had not adorned the hundreds of signs that made up the landscape. Trucks and pickups and even a Cop car passed and tried to persuade me this was a dream or an episode of "The Dukes of Hazzard."

Smells of fast food and diesel oil pungently competed with the heat as I went around the rear of the gas station to see if I could find a toilet, rehearsing in my head that if I were to ask directions I should say "bathroom."

As I rounded the corner of the building I saw a large muscular guy, in a white vest, leaning against the wall about eight feet away.

"Wassup man," he said, cool as you like, a relaxed look on his face. "Hello," I said. "Nice fella," I thought. It was then that I realised that his girlfriend was the reason he was enjoying a moment of relaxation as she dined on the biggest willy I had ever seen in my life. She took a momentary respite and delicately dabbed her mouth with a serviette. The word "napkin" popped into my head. She turned to me, looked straight into my eyes and said, "Grab yourself a Coke, Honey, while I tend to this gentleman. You're such a cutie." The gentleman smiled and closed his eyes.

"No, no, no rush, take your time," I managed to say, sounding welsher than I ever had in my life, before backing up around the corner and running as quickly as I could back to the bus with my tiny penis. "Americans are very polite," I decided.

The journey to my drop off point was only another hour away as I marvelled in the landscape of a thousand movies. After about a half an hour, I was the only one on the bus with the driver. The roads soon became single laned and the dual carriageway turned into what seemed to me a dirt track based on the plume of dust that was constantly visible through the back window. The directions sent to me by the camp said that I should get off the bus at a crossroads at the first sign that said Camp Shohola.

Someone would be there to meet me. I started to get a little nervous of missing my stop, so I went to the front of the bus. "Do you mind if I sit here, Drive?" I said in an attempt to gain his help on not missing my stop.

"What the hell do you mean, boy, of course you can't drive. Move further up the bus please, Sir," he shouted in a tone that seemed moments from drawing a large six shooter from his jacket. I was horrified at my miscommunication but soon managed to explain and then we seemed to hit it off rather well. He was an old guy named Zeke and told me he had been a G.I. in Britain during World War II. He told me about the tea dances and the nylon stockings and the chocolate bars that were so highly prized by the "Brits." He talked of how he had nearly stayed in Britain and how he'd fallen in love with an usherette from Dagenham called Annie.

My crossroads came and went as Zeke's stories continued and it was not for another fifteen minutes that he realised, halfway through a story about finding a German helmet on a battlefield in France with the head still in it, that we had gone too far.

"I'll drop you here, son. It's only about ten miles. We just passed a gas station, you'll find a payphone there, you can call your camp and they can pick you up," said Zeke, very casually.

Ok, compared to being shot at by a Panzer, in a bunker, on a French battlefield, thousands of miles from home with the blood of your buddies splattered across your face, this wasn't a big deal but to me, at that moment, the arse fell out of my world. I had no other option than to say my goodbyes and get off the bus.

I watched as Sergeant Bokino withdrew the infantry from this particular skirmish to, yet again, fight another day.

I brushed the fine dust from my clothes from the skid of the tyres as the bus pulled away. I turned, struggled into my rucksack, and started walking back to the gas station. I must have been walking for about twenty minutes, constantly predicting that I would be able to see my destination after the next undulation of the road but to no avail. It was now early evening, and the sun was very low in the sky, the temperature had dropped and so I stopped to get a jumper out of my backpack.

 Just at that moment I heard a loud rustle in the dense tree line on the side of the road. I stood very still and tried to adjust my vision to see if I could make out anything in the forest.

There it was again, louder this time and a little more frantic. "Hello," I said, not expecting or receiving a reply. There was the noise again, with an added cracking of a branch.

I decided, in American horror film tradition, to investigate. Slowly, I crouched under the branch line and entered the trees. The difference in the light was in total contrast to the roadside. The smell of the pine needles and sap was momentarily uplifting until I saw, in front of me, the unexpected and early conclusion of my quest.

Laying on the ground in front of me was, what I thought at first, a large horse but after a jerking head movement it revealed an enormous set of antlers. The animal was without any fight or motivation to get to its feet and as I approached it opened its eyes and watched me, trustingly, as I got closer.

The stag's breathing was noticeable now and its whole body rose and fell as it laboured to fill and empty its lungs. Its mouth was closed, however, and a long over-pinked tongue appeared, unnaturally from the side of its mouth. It was then I realised the gulps of rasping breath were coming from its throat which had a large cut in the windpipe. It struck me that it was too neat not to be the work of a human and done after hitting the unfortunate animal in some sort of road accident where the stag had come off much worse. It had been done with some sort of best intentions but right here, right now this magnificent beast was in pain and only I could help put it out of its misery. I had spent my life avoiding killing anything whatsoever.

My friends, growing up, had revelled in dispatching fish, rabbits, crows, and pigeons but I never had the stomach for it, hated it in fact, and I was even guilty of getting up in the rosy glow of lingering darkness to release said rabbits from the snares I had collaborated in setting only hours before, even releasing Mrs Isiah's tabby one early morn.

I knew that the only thing to do, the right thing to do was to help this wounded animal by ending its pain. I looked around for a suitable weapon. A steel bar, a concrete post. Neither of these could be found and so I eventually settled for a large, old fence post with a darkened bitumen end that had previously been in the ground. I spoke gently to the stag with some last words that were more for me than him in some final attempt of forgiveness.

His large, brown eyes watched me continually as I got into position.

One large strike to the base of the skull should do it, I thought, clean and simple. The stag sensed my anguish and closed its eyes, its breathing noticeably slower.

I decided on the exact target, raised the post in two hands and forced myself to keep my eyes open, bringing the hardened post down as hard as I could, making exact contact with the desired area. The sound was more of a dull thud than I was expecting.

Instead of the desired effect, my failed attempt at mercy had the opposite effect as life coursed through his body, in fear, shock and panic. A large patch of fur had been knocked off the skull and the pinkness of the flesh screamed through. Not strong enough to stand or move its head, the Stag thrashed its legs about as I repeated and repeated the action with the equal and opposite reaction. Tears streamed down my face as I tried to increase my effort, but it really was not having the effect for which I had prayed.

At my worst point of frenzy came a moment of clarity. I dropped to my knees, took my jumper and, with my eyes closed, held it over the cut in the stag's throat with the full force of my knee. The thrashing stopped, the breathing slowed and after about a minute or so, with me weeping and whispering words that I hoped would be short lived, the stag eventually passed, and I fell back sobbing like an infant's first taste of disappointment. I lay there for ages, my breathing replacing the Stag's as I recovered from the day's desperate exertions.

My mind fell desperately into an abyss of sadness and regret. Sadness that I was not at home with my brothers, in my bedroom, with the love and the comforts of home.

Regret that I had ever come to this bloody country, I hated it, the bigness, the emptiness and the stupid, knob sucking, fucking people.

I sobbed until I had nothing left and after that I put on my blood-stained jumper, re-joined the roadside, and continued along the road. It was dark now and two more miles still did not reveal the gas station as the light faded fast to a monochrome contrast between the sky and the trees.

I was so incredibly sad, lost in body and soul.

I was devoid of any excitement for adventure and experience that had filled my life for the last few months. What was I to do? I had no means to call the camp, no idea where it was and nowhere to stay and not a single vehicle had passed all day. I kept walking until the darkness had draped the trees in anthracite black and the only light was the unfamiliar moon hanging low in the sky. Through a break in the trees, I saw the moon's reflection. It was a building of some sort with small, symmetrical windows and the arched frame, painted white, making it stand out from the ghost of its structure. I walked further up the road and found a small path leading, I hoped, to the building beyond. I could just make out the foot worn walkway and followed it to the front of the doorless barn.

I ventured inside, tired now from my long days' travel and it was approaching thirty-six hours since I had last slept. Inside the barn there was a vertical ladder along the wall that must have led to a loft, so I climbed it immediately, without hesitation, felt the soft hay beneath my feet, took my rucksack off, laid down and slept without ever wanting to wage war against this day again.

The power of sunlight is incredible. When I woke up with the sunrise the next morning, the shards of light seemed almost touchable as they angled into the barn, intensifying the dust from the hay which had provided me with faultless comfort and rest. Gone were the demons from the night before, the doubts, the darkness. Back was the excitement and the anticipation driving me onto the next challenge. It was early, incredibly early but I had no idea what the time was as I never wore a watch, entirely because I didn't own one.

Back out on the road I continued to try and find the, by now, mystical gas station. Then casually, as if it happened every two minutes, a truck went past. I put my thumb out and it stopped. I got in and the guy, returning from a hunting trip, gave me a lift right to the gates of the camp. The only memorable aspect of our ten-mile journey was the fact that his shotgun was in the foot well of the passenger side. The dangerous end was pointing at my face. I spent the whole journey very worried that a pothole in the road would result in the inconvenient removal of my frontal lobe.

With my head, and the rest of me for that matter, intact, I waved my last goodbyes to my new best friend and turned to face Camp Shohola. It was perfect. It was everything I thought it would be. The tall pines surrounded a lake with wooden jetties in the foreground and sandy beaches visible in the distance. The log cabins and stone built reception all contributed to the illusion that this was still a dream and I would awake at any moment, but this was my dream and at that moment I was more determined to dream it than I ever had before, my summer waited patiently as I took one last look at the road I had travelled then I walked through the gates towards the reception.

Now, before we go any further, I feel I have not been completely honest with you. You see, you would be forgiven in thinking that this wonderful adventure in waiting was to play out in the traditional way with good guys and bad guys and a love interest etc, and I promise you there is a large dollop of that but there is one aspect that I must bring your attention to that I have not mentioned before: the way I was dressed. It is worth mentioning here the huge contrasting cultural differences between growing up in a small Welsh mining village in the nineteen eighties and the conservative culture of America of the same time. British pop music ruled the world, and its fashions were moving so fast that in Britain and my hometown of Neath, what was cool now would be considered old news a month later.

In contrast, middle America was very set in its ways. They celebrated being the best you can be in a contest where everyone wore the same type of "uniform". Being the best part of a team was the aim and being an individual was viewed with suspicion and I am sorry to say, in some cases, hostility.

I, on the other hand, wanted to stand out, to celebrate my individualism. To be cool, fashionable and "with it." Whatever my motivation, in hindsight, as I walked into Camp Shohola, I looked like a complete twat. I had skin-tight white Levi jeans on with white espadrilles, a white tee shirt that said "Choose Life" on it from Neath Market and my shoulder length hair was so back combed that it made my head three times the size that it should have been. To complete the effect, I had a hooped gold earring in each ear. I was, in essence, my hero, George Michael, the epitome, as far as I was concerned, of a macho, red blooded male in search of romance and adventure.

I was a "Young Gun", and I was going for it. As I picture myself walking down that drive, I cannot help hearing the intro music to "Club Tropicana" in my head.

Before I got closer, I could see someone swimming towards the landing dock near the reception so headed to meet them as they got out of the water and towelled down. He smiled as I approached.

"Hi there, you must be Lyndon, I'm Kit Barger and this is my summer camp," he said, holding out his hand to greet me. "We were a little worried about you and I called your emergency number. I spoke to your friend Charlie who said we shouldn't worry, and you would turn up eventually. He was right."

I had put Charlie's number as my emergency contact as he was the only one I knew with a phone, who would give a shit if anything happened to me but also not panic. "He could have panicked a little bit," I thought.

"Hi Kit, sorry I'm late arriving." I said, desperate to tell him of my trauma but deciding not to. He stood there, a man in his fifties with the incredible physique of a man thirty years his junior, emphasised even further by his bushy grey beard.

"Well, you are here now. You are Welsh, right? "Yes Sir," I said, trying to fit in. "You play Rugby?" he continued.

"I've played a lot of rugby, Kit, yes, it's our national sport," I beamed, so pleased to be welcomed so heartily, even though George Michael would not have been many people's first choice for their starting XV in any rugby match I could think of. "Well, I have it by very good authority that you guys are some of the toughest sonsabitches in the world. Let's get you settled in," he concluded.

And settle in, I did. Over the next few weeks or so I met some great people and grew to love the cabin I shared with a dozen kids from wealthy families. Summer camp was fantastic, my days were filled with coaching the kids in soccer, which most of them were terrible at. The American counsellors were not great at football either but were incredibly fit, and immediately my fitness increased ten-fold, getting the closest I would ever get to a six pack which seemed to be standard issue at the camp. The food was amazing, and, maybe because I craved it so badly because of the amount of energy I was burning up or the fact that the portion sizes were always more than enough, I began to try things that I would never have at home.

Newfound favourites like meatloaf and tortillas tantalised my tastebuds whilst I found out what words like zucchini and cantaloupe meant after hearing them so many times on American TV shows.

Any spare time I had was spent writing home to tell all of my new, wonderful life. Gone was my "Wham" tribute act and in its place was a tanned, relaxed new me who was living the dream.

There was one fly in the ointment however, a sixteen stone, "bluebottle" called Chet who, at six foot two was an extremely formidable foe to have indeed. He was, I believe, an American Football player who had been coming to the camp since he was a kid and very much saw himself as head counsellor. Chet had a particular dislike for my earrings, which was now only one.

A girl at the sister camp, Camp Netemis, had given me a dangly one with a cross and a snake on it, which coincidentally was identical to the one Rob Lowe had in the current hit movie "St Elmo's Fire."

It was causing, if I do say so myself, a bit of a stir amongst the female counsellors. This is how I met and got talking to Gabrielle, who had lightly teased me about it, which I thought was funny. Chet had gone for a completely different approach.

Chet referred to me, whenever he saw me as "Faggot," or "Faggoty Faggot" and sometimes even "Faggoty Fag Boy." My witty comebacks were not having any effect, whatsoever. If anything, they had an adverse effect and seemed to just increase the ferocity at which he spat the insults at me. The situation was also not helped by the fact that he was very smitten on Gabrielle before I appeared on the scene but was too dumb arsed to speak to her.

This went on for a week or so and was eased only by me never being within a hundred yards of him. I must admit, he had got me worried, frightened even. I considered myself a lover not a fighter and it would be forty years or so until my wife would let me into the thinly veiled secret that I was not much of a lover either.

So, I avoided him the best I could and tried to get through my slightly tarnished summer.

On our evening off, Gabrielle and I decided to go to the local bar, "Frank's," who turned a blind eye to the underaged counsellors having a few beers.

Local, by the way, was fifteen miles from the camp. It seemed to me to be the archetypal American bar with neon beer signs and motorbike parts adorning the walls, full of wax bottles to smash over fake biker gang's heads or polystyrene tables to throw them onto.

We were having a game of nine ball, where I was showboating the ultimately useless skills I had picked up in the sticky snooker halls of the Neath valley, when a crowd of counsellors came in that I recognised as Chet's cronies, who walked past us and disappeared round the corner. They all looked like they had been drinking before getting to "Frank's." I breathed a premature sigh of relief before then seeing Chet and his main disciple coming through the door. I deliberately played a shot so that my back was to him in the vain hope he would not see me. I thought I had gotten away with it until I heard his, oh so now familiar, voice.

"Well, if it ain't Mr Faggoty Faggot and his Faggoty earing," slurred Chet.

Here is the thing about Americans and the Welsh, well the youngsters anyway. American teenagers cannot drink. I guess whilst they were trying out for the cheerleading team or trying to make it as quarterback we were drinking "White Lightning" cider at the local rec or swigging flagons of "Strongbow" down by the canal. This doesn't seem like any sort of advantage to be proud of, but I would soon be very grateful for my misspent youth.

"Good evening Butdy," I swallowed. I had not mastered the subtle difference between "butty" and "buddy." "Mr Faggoty, Fag Boy, enjoys playing with balls, now there's a surprise," laughed Chet, turning to his right-hand man who unconvincingly laughed moments later.

My stomach was turning over inside, and I had a flash of caving his head in with the cue that was in my hand.

That is what Charlie would have done, marauding through the bar, opening eyebrows and fattening lips as he went. I wished he were there now.

"I just want a quiet game of pool, Chet, just leave it out, Butt," I tried to reason with him.

"So, you like my butt do you, Fag boy?" said Chet in huge self-congratulations at his first ever original quip. "I bloody walked into that one," I thought.

"Leave him alone, Chet," said Gabrielle, which guaranteed my annihilation. I knew Chet's next move. He would insult her, and I would have to try and stop this resulting in a full-blown beating. I would be thrown around the room and publicly humiliated, that was how it was to go. I decided to spare Gabrielle whatever was slowly formulating in Chet's brain and rely on the only weapon I had left. It had gotten me out of trouble more times than it had gotten me in, but I saw no other option than to go full guns blazing and at least save some dignity.

My weapon of choice, of course, was my smart mouth. My finest asset and my most heinous enemy. "Bollocks to it," I decided in my head.

I took a deep breath and launched into, "Listen here, you fucking, "Back to the Future" Biff, bastard, with your huge forehead and breath like an old man's arse. If you don't fuck the fuck off, I'm going to split your head in two and then shove this stick so far up your arse that your mama is gonna be whistling dixie." I held the pool stick upside down in both hands and held it aloft to stop my hands from shaking.

"Where the hell had that come from?" I wondered.

I had started off on a South Wales council estate, went a little bit Ronnie and Reggie, then ended up in the deep South, possibly, Alabama. Gabrielle looked at me, she had a very puzzled look on her face.

I could only shrug a bewildered response. Chet's face was very disturbing. He was just starting to comprehend, with the delay of a slow mind hampered by alcohol. I watched as his expression changed from complete bemusement to unbridled anger. He moved towards me. "You Goddamn…" then he was halted in his tracks by Frank.

"You boys take that outside," shouted Frank. "Outside, now Faggot," screamed Chet and headed for the door. "Good luck, Kid," said Frank.

"Can you get our things, Gabrielle?" I said in complete resignation. She nodded and headed for the bar where our jackets were over the backs of some barstools.

Chet's wingman squealed with delight as he ran over to the bowling alley, where the unholy trinity remained uninformed.

I headed outside quickly, to try and talk Chet out of it or beg him or bribe him before anyone came out. I was two steps behind him as he bumped into the door and the frame; he really was drunk.

What happened next happened very quickly.

At the top of the three steps down onto the car park made up of compacted dry mud and gravel, Chet tripped, just a little at first then his size thirteen feet tried desperately to play catch but there was only one winner, gravity. Chet tumbled down the steps and lay on his back.

"Salvation," I thought, praying he was unconscious.

Then a sound to curdle my blood, Chet started to laugh, a drunken laugh that proved, beyond any doubt, he was not the worse for wear from his fall.

"You ok, Chet?" I said in the vain hope that we could all laugh about it and have a drink inside.

"Help me up, Faggot, I'm gonna kick your ass," came the response. That was the moment I gave into my fear and self-preservation kicked in.

I looked behind me to see Chet's buddies a foot or so from the inner doors heading in our direction. I hurriedly walked up to Chet, took his outstretched, inebriated hand in my left hand and just as he was relying on my strength to haul him up, I betrayed him and hit him as hard as I could in the face three times in quick succession. As the final blow hit Chet square on the nose, I saw his eyes close, reminding me momentarily of my Stag and its final breath. His head made a thud against the ground.

"Shit, I hoped I haven't killed him," I thought. My heart was near explosion as Chet's grip went limp as he, thankfully, lay unconscious on the gravel, his chest moving effortlessly up and down. More familiar imagery came flooding in. God, my hand was hurting and upon inspection I could see broken skin on three of my knuckles that I presumed had been a badly placed blow against Chet's teeth instead of his nose.

I now prepared for the incoming showdown with Chet's gang as they burst onto the scene. The four of them stopped immediately in their tracks, like they had witnessed a miracle. Gabrielle was just behind them, and her reaction was equally dumbfounded.

I realised at that point that to all intents and purposes, the scene they had all fallen upon was one where I had whooped Chet's arse, in a fair fight, man on man. To avoid any further trouble from any of the group I decided I had no choice but to bluff it out. "What the fuck are you looking at?" I shouted, praying I could pull this off. "Get this dickhead out of here."

And with that they all gathered up Chet and loaded him in the back of a pickup truck and avoiding my direct gaze, drove away towards camp.

Gabrielle was next to me, "Well, he wasn't expecting that, was he?" she said, with the hint of suspicion in her eyes.

"Neither was I, Bab. Let's get a drink," I put my hand round her shoulder and kissed her on the head. Frank was at the top of the steps. "Well, son, I never thought you had it in you. Let's get that hand looked at," he said calmly. "Well, Frank, things are never as they seem," I smiled, pushing my luck outrageously.

I am tempted to describe Frank as looking and sounding like "Sam Elliot" from some of my favourite eighty's movies, but I guess "Danny DeVito's" less articulate cousin would be more accurate as a description.

We had a fine night indeed as a few of the locals joined in with my moment of victory, a huge gang of counsellors arrived and swelled the throng with tales from the camp spreading like wildfire of my showdown with Chet, ranging from a Jackie Chan back flip to a Patrick Swayze roundhouse. I enquired after Chet, appearing empathetic, but was told he was put to bed in the sick bay for the evening but was sleeping off his drunken misadventure.

Always in the back of my mind, that night, I knew that tomorrow my luck would finally run out. Chet was surely going to get his revenge, telling everyone I had sucker punched him and worse still, beating the bejesus out of me. But that was tomorrow, so, that night, I sang and drank and danced like a man who faced the hangman in the morning.

Bollocks to it.

Waking up the next morning was not an experience I ever want to repeat. As I lay there in my bunk, my first task was to try and remove the invisible spike that someone had driven through my forehead, trapping me in bed.

The smallest movement sent inconceivable shards of pain shooting through my head and the rest of my pathetic body.

184

I lay there for a while as flashbacks betrayed the previous evening. Like the teleprompter from "World of Sport" with Dickie Davies, images and updates came flooding in. Did I really sing "Another one bites the dust" whilst standing on the tables at "Franks?" If I did then I must have also sung, "Delilah," "The Green, Green Grass of Home" and "Hen wlad fy nhadau" - they usually came as a full set. I started to remember re-enacting my fight scene with Chet, for the amusement of the crowd. Where I had given him one last chance to walk away, warning him of the can of "whoopass" he was about to open, before sidestepping a couple of haymakers and then dispatching him with the clinical efficiency of a ninja with a part time job in an abattoir.

What had I done and why had I done it? Surely today would be my last day at the camp.

I would be sought out by Chet, beaten to within an inch of my life and then humiliated in front of everyone for being a coward and a charlatan. I feared the latter as much as the prior. I managed to get myself up and struggled into the shower area with a fistful of paracetamol downed with the first mouthful of water from the showerhead. After a while I felt a little better and got into my clothes, went outside, and joined the entire camp as they completed the daily raising of the flag. Nobody seemed to have missed me and at the end of the ceremony I started to move to my first activity of the day which was Wood shop.

I thanked my lucky stars it was not something more physical. Still in a daze, I had not noticed someone come up behind me. I spun round as their hand was placed on my shoulder, ready to flail my arms or run or beg for mercy. It was only Duncan Barger, Kit's son, a lovely lad who had become a good friend of mine.

"My dad wants to see you in his cabin, to discuss your evening last night," said Duncan, a playful smile on his face. "Oh, ok, cheers mate," was all I could muster.

So here it was, the finale of my summer. Not only would the truth come out, but I would also lose the respect of a man I had become very fond of indeed. A man that personified everything that is great about Americans: their honesty, their integrity, and their sense of fair play. As I walked to Kit's impressive cabin, to his office adorned with achievement and camp history I was extremely low indeed. As I walked up the steps to the main door, I saw Chet standing in Kit's office. Kit was sitting at his desk.

Like several times in my life up until that point, I had no control over what was about to happen, I gave myself over to the moment, knocked the door and entered upon invitation.

The sound that greeted me was not of the eerie silence of shame or the preparation of pending doom, but a noise that I was not expecting, a sound that was so familiar to me but somehow out of context and momentarily unplaceable. On a small tv in the corner was playing a grainy video of a game of rugby from the seventies.

I recognised the sound of the crowd and the excited voice of the commentator. It was a video I had seen many times and almost knew it verbatim. It was the famous game between Bridgend and The All Blacks where JPR Williams was stamped in the face by New Zealand prop John Ashworth in what could have been a career ending injury.

JPR had defiantly ran from the field with blood streaming from his face with no chance of return only to do exactly that minutes later, bandaged, and beautiful. It has become legendary in Wales folklore as a metaphor for the hardness of the Welsh working man and our "never give up" attitude.

As I entered the office Kit leaned over and switched off the tv. "Hi Lyndon, come in would ya, stand here for a moment." said Kit, friendly but neutral.

I stood there beside Chet who was looking forward only, head slightly downturned. I dare not look at him and without intention aped his stance with my hands behind my back. "Here it comes," I thought.

"Lyndon," began Kit, "I would like to apologise on behalf of Camp Shohola for the way you have been treated since your arrival. I have received incredibly positive feedback from many counsellors on your hard work and cheerful attitude with the campers, they really seem to like you. I have also, however, heard reports that you have had to endure the most horrendous antagonism and disrespect during your time with us that I am both disappointed and disgusted by." He looked long and hard at Chet whose head sank lower.

Kit continued, "Please be assured that this is not our way at Camp Shohola, and you have my word it will not happen again, though after last night's events I believe the issue has been dealt with. Chet here, has something to say."

I was flabbergasted and stood there incredulous of what had just been said. I had never been shown such respect and fair play before and my emotions started to get the better of me. I felt tears well in my eyes. Ironically, Chet was my salvation.

"Lyndon," Chet began, turning to face me for the first time. His eye socket was badly bruised and there was a large cut on his lip. His tooth had a small corner missing but his nose looked gloriously untouched. I questioned my aim that night, which seemed to be a little off, after all.

"I am so deeply sorry for my behaviour during your time in Camp. I realise now that I was wrong to treat you this way. You have acted with dignity and honour, and I deserved everything you dished out last night. If you give me another chance I will try and make amends." Chet then turned away and bowed his head again. Then it hit me, Chet had no Idea what happened last night, he could not remember.

The stupid lummox was apologising to me for my cowardly behaviour, punching him in the face when he had fallen over. This really was a bizarre situation.

Kit took over, "I have got Chet to pack his things and have told him on your say so, he will be on the next bus home." I looked down to see Chet was standing next to his trunk, the sort owned by every camp regular. "So, I guess it's down to you Lyndon?" Kit concluded.

This really was too much; I was half expecting Candid Camera to burst in and tell me this was a set up. Could things really have worked out so well for me? Could I really have snatched victory from the jaws of such terrible defeat? I was overcome with an enormous guilt, I could not let them believe this charade any longer, I had to tell them the truth, even though it would mean the ruination of my newfound reputation and respect. It was the right thing to do.

"Bollocks to it," I thought.

"That's alright boyo, no hard feelings," I said as I turned to Chet with a huge smile on my face. Chet grabbed my hand with both of his, a relief on his face akin to a death row pardon. "Back to work then, Chet," said Kit, smiling forgivingly, enjoying the fact I had passed his test.

Chet picked up his trunk and was gone in seconds but not before thanking me again profusely. In the quiet of the office, Kit laughed at the success of his plan.

"Chet is a good guy really, just needed a lesson in life which it sounds like you taught him. I was explaining when you came in that you Welsh guys are tough. I played a bit of rugby at college, and I met a few of your compatriots. God they could drink and fight. Good times." He pointed to a picture on his wall with a young Kit surrounded by men I did not recognise beyond their tell-tale beer bellies and seventies moustaches that could easily have been a Pontypool front row fancy dress outing.

Kit believed the common stereotype of the Welsh, that we are accomplished in the arts of rugby, drinking, and fighting. For many, this may have been true but in my case, I did not excel in any of these disciplines. I smiled and to avoid any resurging emotional state I said, "Thanks Kit."

"And regarding your earring, I guess some are too young to remember the Summer of Love," he pointed to another picture of a younger Kit at what I assumed was Woodstock, he was bare chested and dressed in a suede brown waistcoat with colourful braiding with shoulder length hair, a headband and a dangly, feathered earring. "Thank you again, Kit," I laughed and left his office, my earring blowing in the wind.

The rest of the summer was amazing, full of sunlight dappled through the tall pines contrasting with the endless childhood laughter of the campers.

I made so many friends and the comradery of the other councillors made it a summer that would be difficult to ever forget. Chet became a bit of a pain in the arse for a different reason. He hung around me a bit too much and tried a bit too hard to be my friend. I was nice to him but found myself avoiding him once again.

Highlights of the summer were tubing on the Potomac River and paddleboarding around the lake on endless days of sunshine and stillness.

On one excursion to Poughkeepsie, New York State a group of us went to see a band that I had never heard of called "The Psychedelic Furs," who had a soundtrack song from the hot film of the moment, "Pretty in Pink." It was my first ever concert and I very soon realised it wasn't my sort of thing. I sneaked out after the first song and decided to have a look about the town. The theatre across from our concert was highlighting new comedians, much more my thing. I bought a ticket for six dollars and went in to see the show that was now in its second half.

The comedian that was on stage was incredible. His energy and skilled use of the stage took my breath away. His crazy voices and mimicry had me laughing uncontrollably within seconds and this continued throughout his routine even though most of the Americanisms were beyond me. I recognised him somehow then as, after a while, he went into a character he did on a sitcom he was in, and the penny dropped.

The sitcom was "Mork and Mindy" and standing on the stage in front of me was the comedy legend, Robin Williams. I was honoured to be there that evening and have been grateful ever since to have witnessed his genius.

The end of my wonderful Summer Camp experience was looming and together a group of friends from the camp and I decided to buy an old van from the camp that had been left under some trees for the last five years. The idea was to travel down the east coast of America to Florida then part our ways and continue with our own adventures. My last adventure was to be flying from Florida to Philadelphia on an inland flight to spend a week with Gabrielle and her family which I was really looking forward to.

The little green van was caked in the debris of neglect but soon cleaned up to reveal boggle eyed headlights and a big smiley grille on the front. The others decided to call our new little friend "Jeremiah" after the song "Joy to the world," which had made a resurgence that summer.

I was clearly delighted and after a little tinkering with the engine and a new battery it croaked into life, probably because it had a mere twenty thousand miles on the clock, and not because of my mechanical prowess.

I said my temporary goodbyes to Gabrielle with the promise of seeing her in two weeks' time.

The last night at the camp was full of heartfelt goodbyes and laughter of the great memories we had made.

There was even a tearful goodbye from Chet who, it seems, had become very fond of me indeed. The tears were his and not mine. As we said our final farewell, I looked at the stud earring in his ear and chuckled to myself, "you stupid twat."

Our two weeks in "Jeremiah" were too action packed to document but let's just say that our fourteen days travelling through Washington State, Virginia, North Carolina, South Carolina, Georgia and finally into Florida contained a car chase after attending an illegal tobacco auction at midnight, a week as guests of one of the richest restaurateurs in America, a fight with a particularly angry racoon. This time I lost. I sold most of my clothes on Daytona Beach as I'd run out of money and had a three day stay at a Hari Krishna commune, together with orange robes and tinkly bells.

It was with genuine sadness I finally said my last farewell to Piers, Gabby, and Mark at Florida Airport, but was also filled with the excitement of seeing Gabrielle again.

As "Jeremiah" hopped away into the Florida swamps, I threw my trusty rucksack onto my shoulders and headed towards my flight to my last week in the United States.

I was completely broke by this point and was also looking forward to the fifty pounds that would be waiting for me at Gabrielle's. My Mam had sent it by Air Mail, and I had had extraordinarily little to eat since the lentil soup provided by Buddha himself at the commune some two days earlier. I managed to swipe a half-eaten burger off one of the discarded trays at a burger joint inside the Airport and was set up for my flight. In just over an hour, I had arrived in Philadelphia and was on the train to Wynnewood, a pretty suburb just outside the city. The whole rail system ran on an honesty policy where you jump on and pay the guard when he eventually makes his rounds. I combated this by getting off the train whenever he appeared and getting on the next one, which ran every ten minutes or so. It seemed to work well. I was amazed by the station names on the way to Wynnewood.

I passed through Bethesda, Bryn Mawr and Narberth enroute and a friendly passenger told me it was because Pennsylvania had been a pioneer mining community and lots of Welsh miners had settled there first and hence were responsible for the Welsh names of the towns. Little did I know that this small piece of information would come in very handy, very soon.

I had turned down Gabrielle's offer of picking me up from the station in favour of following her directions and walking the two miles to her house. I marvelled at the beautiful houses and magnificent town planning of the parks and communal areas.

Even though I had been in America for over two months I still had to pinch myself occasionally to prove I was there. The area seemed extremely wealthy, and I started to wonder what Gabrielle's house would be like. Her Mom was a teacher and her dad a University Professor, so I was expecting it to be nice and I wasn't disappointed. As I walked up the drive of the leafy garden of the huge frontage to their large house in brown and cream stone, I momentarily compared it to the semi-detached council house I had left some nine weeks earlier, in which I would never live again.

Gabrielle was waiting for me with her mom, Lynne, and her younger sister Sophie. They gave me such a lovely welcome and soon we were sitting in their typically American kitchen talking of the differences in our cultures.

Gabrielle's surname was Davies and it turned out that her Dad's Dad was first generation Welsh and had come over after the war, never to return to Wales.

Gabrielle's Dad was immensely proud of his Celtic roots and indeed was part of an American Welsh Society in the area which was his main hobby, being a history professor and all that.

It was also slipped into the conversation that he was very much against my visit but that I should just leave that for Lynne to sort out. I sensed they were all a little worried about it.

"Does he know I'm Welsh?" I asked Gabrielle. "I didn't know you were till just now, you Brits sound all the same to me," she giggled. I made a mental note to myself, and we waited for Gabrielle's Dad's return from work.

His arrival was unexpectedly emotional, for me more than the others. He first hugged and kissed his wife with a wonderful affection, then both his daughters in turn, not hurrying or going through the motions but with real love and the satisfaction of all being together, even though it must have been a daily occurrence. Even the dog, Sparky, got in on the action after patiently waiting his turn. I decided, at that very moment, that if I ever had a family, this is how I would greet them, love them, and keep them safe from the rent man or the breath of the beer towel.

Mr Davies was not a tall man but held himself like one. He was dressed smartly in a tweed jacket with corduroy trousers and a chequered shirt. The patches on his elbows and the black, sensible glasses confirmed, if any doubt remained, that he was, very much, from the world of academia.

"And who is this fine, young gentleman?" he said finally, a short glance to Lynne gave away the fact that he was uncomfortable with the idea that his seventeen-year-old daughter should be having a boyfriend to stay, but still smiled with a genuine greeting.

Before anyone could speak on my behalf I said, "Hello Mr Davies, I'm Lyndon Jeremiah, I'm very pleased to meet you and thank you for letting me stay, diolch yn fawr." I then waited to see if there was any bardic response, but there was nothing.

"You are very welcome, Lyndon. Jeremiah? That is an interesting name and please, continue to call me Mr Davies." he smiled.

"Dad!" squealed Gabrielle. "Darling!" said Lynne, they all laughed together.

"That's a good line," I thought to myself, but I was ready to try again.

"Yes," I persevered, "Jeremiah is a very unusual name where I come from."

"Is that so? Is it Hebraic?" said Mr Davies with interest.

I was struggling with this one as I was teetering on the edge of my education to date and found myself looking into the ravine of stupidity but so wanted to continue the conversation on his level and not simply blurt out "I'm bloody Welsh, mun." I continued with unabated bravery to the noticeable bewilderment of Gabrielle and her mom.

"It's certainly biblical, the English replaced local names they could not pronounce and replaced them with names from The Bible when they finally, successfully invaded." Again, I avoided saying the word Wales as I wanted it to be his discovery, but I was getting a little desperate now.

"Ah! A fellow historian, we should talk later, at dinner," and with that slight pacification, he was gone.

"Damn it," I thought, "I missed my chance." Dinner was wonderful, all gathered around a small, elegant table with the vegetables that accompanied my newfound favourite, meatloaf, served in pretty china tureens.

Grace was short, informal, and seemed the most natural thing in the world to me, which, of course, it wasn't.

I felt that Mr Davies' early friendliness had dissipated as the reality of having a stranger staying in his house for a week was dawning on him.

A stranger whose sole motivation, no doubt, was to corrupt his daughter in sins of the flesh. Thank goodness I had removed my earring. Time to fight back. "So, Gabrielle tells me you are off to University next month, Lyndon," said Lynne as conversation starter, "To study industrial design, isn't it?"

"Why didn't she ask which University? I would have said The University of Wales, Lynne, thank you for asking," I cursed silently to myself. "Yes, that's right, Lynne," I said lamely.

"So, you are not a history major, that's a shame," announced Mr Davies to a chastising glance from Lynne, who then gave a kindly smile in my direction. I considered my response. "Come on Lyndon, this is what you do. You move into people's lives and assume their ways, through learned behaviour. You use small bits of information, expand them and you fit in, you make people like you, you are good at this." Then the fog cleared. I said slowly, "I am afraid not, but I do like history. I was particularly interested to see the names of the stations as I came from the city to Wynnewood. All named after Welsh towns, no doubt by the miners that settled in the pioneer towns of Pennsylvania. It felt like I was home in Wales again." There was a stifled giggle from Lynne, who hid it well enough to let me know she knew exactly what I was trying to achieve.

Gabrielle smiled as if she was impressed but unlike her mom, she was oblivious to my motives. "Are you Welsh, Lyndon? I had no idea, you should have said," exclaimed Mr Davies. Lynne used the clearing of the table to disguise her latest fall from grace.

"You ok, hun?" he enquired. "I'm fine darling, you must tell Lyndon about our Welsh connections," she just managed to remark before disappearing to the sanctuary of the kitchen. And that was that.

Mr Davies transformed into an enthused, animated creature that took me a little by surprise. This was clearly something he was extremely enthusiastic about, but to my surprise I found that I enjoyed it too. There was not much I didn't know about Wales's part in the Industrial revolution thanks entirely to Mr Brian Davies (no relation), my inspirational history teacher and form master at Llangatwg Comprehensive School and I was able to contribute intelligently to the breathless one man show that Mr Davies gave us on how Pennsylvania's industrial past was built on the expertise of Wales's finest. Next, I was taken to Mr Davies' den, where the walls were adorned with American Welsh insignias and grainy old photos of Welsh miners and their apparel. There were awards and certificates documenting a life well lived in the wonderful world of education.

When we re-joined the rest of the family in the tv lounge, Mr Davies announced that I was to accompany him in two days' time to his American Welsh society get together.

"It is such a shame that you will be back home in Wales when I give my Lecture to the Society next month. I have been working on it for ages and have taken lots of photographs in all the major historical mining sites in Pennsylvania." he said, with a genuine regret of my upcoming absence. "A real shame," I said, secretly realising that it might be a step beyond my interest levels.

At bedtime, before disappearing into their spare room that was to be my quarters for the week, Gabrielle and I met on the landing for a goodnight kiss.

"I think my dad likes you," she said. "I like him too, he's a lovely man. Goodnight."

The next couple of days were great fun, with malls, bowling alleys and enormous cinema screens that were all new experiences for a valley boy who had never ventured outside his comfort zone before this American adventure.

The evening at Mr Davies' society was pleasant enough too, with lots of hand shaking and smiles. They even welcomed me with their traditional American Welsh salutation. "Aggy, aggy, aggy. Hey, hey, hey." I did not have the heart to tell them it should be…

"Oggy, oggy, oggy. Oi, oi, oi.

Other things missing from the "Welsh" night were faggots and peas, Welsh cakes, copious amounts of beer, singing, more beer, arguments, and a massive brawl. As a conclusion though, this was a blessed relief.

And so, my life changing American summer drew painfully to a conclusion after spending some time with Gabrielle's friends and attending both a baseball and a college football game, to my complete confusion. There was a small opportunity, one windy afternoon when we were alone in her house where we could have consummated our romance, but neither of us were terribly bereft that we did not take it any further. It remains one of the few moments in my life where I made the right decision with regards to those sorts of shenanigans.

And so, after saying my goodbyes to Gabrielle's family the previous evening, with the promise to show them all around Wales on their planned trip in two years' time and a heartfelt hug from all of them including Mr Davies, who, by now regarded me as one of the finest young men he had ever met. Ingrained with honesty, valour, and the sort of partner for his daughter he would have welcomed wholeheartedly into the family. My work here was done.

All that remained was a particularly tearful farewell to Gabrielle on her doorstep and I was on my way back to the train station in Wynnewood, JFK, Britain, Wales, University, and more adventures beyond.

It was that final memory that snapped me back into the conversation with Gabrielle, some thirty-six years later, which had now upgraded to a messenger call rather than by text.

"Photographs, what photographs?" I repeated, this time in person. "You really do not remember? The camera that was in my bedroom, that morning when you left?" cajoled Gabrielle, with a softness in her voice.

I tried to think back. We were alone in the house that morning, I was packing just after a shower. Oh wait, I do remember. I was in her bedroom getting a towel and I saw her camera on her desk. That is right, I thought it would be a ruse to take a few snaps of myself, in the mirror, in my underpants as a little reminder of our great summer. I giggled as I wrote "Hi Gabrielle," backwards on a piece of paper so it was visible in the mirror and poked the corner inside my pants, so it hung down my leg as I snapped away the last four pictures left on the reel.

There were two frontal shots then I got a bit more confident with a side stance, Betty Boop-esque, shot with my little finger on my lips.

I finished with a flourish by orchestrating a rear view shot with my pants slightly lowered with a new sign that read "Cymru am Byth," again written in reverse so it would have the full effect on the processed photographs. The sign dangled provocatively between my legs on a string of paper clips I had found in her desk organiser.

"Oh God, Gab, I do remember. Oh God, please do not tell me that your dad saw them? Only you were supposed to see them." I blurted out. "Oh, he saw them alright, but not in the sense you are thinking of, I didn't show them to him, but he saw them," she explained, clearly enjoying the fact she was able to hand over the obvious burden. "What do you mean? I do not understand," I said incredulously.

Gabrielle continued, "You may want to sit down for this Lyndon. You see, that camera was not mine, it was, in fact, my dad's. He had asked me to take it into the processors as he was busy and wanted the photographs on there for work". "Oh shit," was all I could say.

"It gets worse, it gets so much worse. The photos were for my dad's presentation to the American Welsh society and the pics went straight onto slides which my dad's assistant picked up and, as directed, placed in order into the cassette, ready for the presentation. My Dad did run through them but when he got to the last photograph that correlated with his script. He saw no reason to go any further." Gabrielle was now building this story and executing it to a perfect crescendo that had been years in the planning.

"Bloody shit, I can't bear it, what happened?" I begged. "Well, you will be glad to hear that the presentation was a great success. My Dad, as you know, is very thorough and his research is impeccable. The last slide of his presentation was on the screen when his assistant, as directed, pressed the controller to finish with the crest of the society but as you know, Lyndon, there were a few surprises for the two hundred strong audience that evening."

"No, Gab, surely not, please no," I was running out of horrified verbal responses.

"The first slide, I believe, said 'Hi Gabrielle.' There was a stunned silence which quickly turned to giggles then raucous laughter. My dad, at this point had not realised as he had his back to the screen awaiting his, much deserved, applause. His assistant panicked and tried to skip through the reel but only found `Hi Gabrielle' from a different angle. Again, he tried to hurry through the cassette but found, what my mom still refers to as, "the Marilyn shot."

My dad was now standing dumbstruck in front of the screen whilst the room was filled with hysterical laughter which very

199

soon turned to a standing ovation when my dad's assistant, in a last-ditch attempt to end his hell, skipped to the money shot. "Cymru am Byth," or "Wales forever," as it translates to, which ironically is one of the Society's mottos and was written on the wall alongside the screen. The room, of course, erupted."

"Oh my God, Gabrielle, I am so sorry, I don't know what to say, your poor dad, I feel so terrible," I waited whilst the silence continued.

Eventually Gabrielle spoke. "Ha, ha, you are forgiven now, but it took a while. My dad was furious, of course and refused to ever mention your name again, still has not after all these years. My mom on the other hand thinks the whole thing was hilarious and asks about you sometimes. Sophie thought you were of legendary status and even teased my husband, occasionally, that I should have married that naked Welsh boy."

"Well for what it's worth Gabrielle, I am sorry, although it does seem a series of catastrophic coincidences." I resigned.

"Yes, there were a number of those that summer, Lyndon. Take care and let's stay connected," she signed off, slightly cryptically. "Goodbye Gab," I said, relieved our friendship was still intact.

I considered what I had just heard and the chaos I had caused that summer, the greatest summer of my life. Through the awkward feelings and the questioning of my actions, I smiled and decided I would not have changed a single thing.

Bollocks to it...

Mr Wood

Finding out you are about to become a father is an important moment in the life of any man. Your reaction to this news is dependent on many factors. These can range from your age, financial security, the desperation to start a family, marital status, whether it is planned or unplanned and if you have the support of your partner's parents. If most of these factors are in place, then receiving this monumental news can be the most joyous of your life, filled with loving tears of unbridled happiness and back slapping celebrations. Being partly responsible for the formation of new life and creating an actual new human being is, without any shadow of a doubt, under the right circumstances the greatest sole achievement of a man of any age.

However, if any of these societal safety nets are not in place then this can cause discomfort and worries resulting in mild stress and a reassessment of one's priorities. If you find that you have absolutely none of these wonderful advantages in place then receiving the news that fatherhood is looming can be an unmitigated life ending, "how the shit did this happen?", fucking nightmare.

I remember that evening like it was branded on my forehead. Megan and I were staying in the home of her Auntie Barbie in Banbury in Oxfordshire. She had moved in with Megan's Nan, just so we could have the house to ourselves. Barbie was like Frances de la Tour and Mother Teresa had morphed into one person. By that of course I mean she looked like Frances de la Tour and had the kindness of Mother Teresa, not the other way around. I would hate this tale to hurt anyone's feelings, unless it was my deliberate intention, which in this case, it was not. We were both twenty-one years old and it was the summer that had followed our final year at The University of Wales.

Megs had graduated with high honours in English and History, and I had ended up with, what was commonly known as "a Richard," the third, a third-class honours degree in Three-Dimensional Design.

This was accepted as the very lowest accolade that you could, just barely, consider your three years at university any type of minor success. Of course, I had my list of extenuating circumstances and excuses at the ready, but the truth be told, the course was a year too long for me and I had peaked a year earlier and had struggled to keep my momentum up. I knew this, and still do, was a major flaw in my personality that I would have to limp along with it for the rest of my days and add this to the clashes with authority that came with me "as standard," resulting in my rather tardy qualification. "A Third-Class Honours Degree," was a club whose members included the drunken, the work-shy and the inept. Sometimes its members contained lesser amounts of all these qualities which, upon reflection, was a more accurate summation. On the days I am less self-abusive, I realise that it was not that my effort in the race was lacking, it is just that I was in the wrong race.

Megs had immediately put her hard work to effective use and secured a position with "The Banbury Guardian," as a news reporter and she effortlessly joined adulthood as I watched from my metaphorical monkey bars.
She was a huge and instant success, even getting her own column on the "What's On" section in the local area.

She became a bit of a pin up girl with the soldiers on the local American airbase and started to get letters from a number of them requesting "an afternoon tea" or "a picnic by the river," due mostly,
I suspect, to a beautiful picture of her at the top of her column, rather than "The Yank's" interest in country shows highlighting the size of a particular vegetable or the agility of your prize guinea pig.

One particularly persistent pen pal was a clean cut, close shaved, all American, small town, "Yes Sir, Sargent Sir," officer in the Marine Corps called Captain Bob Dobolina. He even sent photos of himself and even I had to admit he was a much better option than the bargain basement, end of the line, "like a real man, but smaller," that she had dragged, spluttering from the banks of the Severn estuary. It must have been such a tough time for her with so much excitement and stimulation in her life, but I was finding my transfer to big boy land more difficult to comprehend. Some might argue that the paperwork is still not stamped and that there is an incomplete form somewhere, with my details on it, that has slipped down the back of a filing cabinet marked "Maturity Exempt."

I had failed in my attempt to secure a full-time position in my chosen field as a designer after attending two interviews. One with a successful tile manufacturer in which I opened my portfolio the wrong way up and emptied its contents onto the floor, out of order, therefore rendering it, and me, nonsensical throughout.
The other was at a small design firm in Leamington Spa where I talked so much that it was impossible for them to ask me a single question and therefore using up my slot completely, whilst ending up with the panel not knowing anything about me or indeed wanting anything to do with me. I was currently making do with part time work in the area, which in the twilight years of the 1980's there was an abundance of.

I had returned that day from yet another temporary agency job at the local industrial estate. It had been a two-man job where a Black lad called Curtis and I had to strip naked and don paper bodysuits to jump inside a huge vat of catering chocolate where the heating element had failed. Our task was to bucket the molten chocolate out before it set, therefore destroying an expensive machine. Within minutes, our paper suits had disintegrated and me and my new best friend writhed nakedly, waist deep in cooking chocolate.

We both became aware that the health and safety rules in that factory must have insisted on by six supervisors, all of which were female. Curtis and I agreed this was the worst day of our lives by the time we had completed our mission, which had gotten harder and harder as the chocolate did. We stood there, side by side in front of a large mirror in the shower rooms at Lesme Ltd. Both of us were covered in chocolate from head to toe, our hair was matted and flat, weighed down by the hardened confectionary. I was so relieved when Curtis said it first as it had been burning a hole in my brain all day, though I didn't feel it was my place to say it. "You see, mate," he said, "It's true what they say, we are not so different really." It was kind of him, of course, but I was very much aware of one "small" difference.

I had seen him from afar a couple of weeks later in Banbury town centre and had shouted across to him but, time and time again, he seemed to ignore me until I realised that he had his Walkman playing and was blissfully unaware of my continued call for his attention. As he disappeared around the corner, it became obvious that although he had not heard me, my calls across the busy square had caused a vitriolic response from all around me, resulting in angry repercussions and some heated argy bargy. It was at that point I wished that I had remembered Curtis' name and had not spent the last thirty seconds shouting "Hey, Mr Chocolate," and "Yo, Chocolate Boy," at him, on a busy Saturday afternoon, in the middle of that Oxfordshire town.

Megs was home before me that day and was sitting at the small kitchen table. I immediately went over to give her our usual hello kiss when she burst into tears. Through her sobs, interrupted only with huge intakes of breath and crashing, vibrating out breaths, she eventually told me she was pregnant. At first, I do not think I really took it in. My first, knee jerk reaction was to deal with the fact she was so upset. After three years together, I had caused this reaction many times, though a few were beyond my control or responsibility.

Without time to think or to process I found myself telling her it was ok, that everything would be fine, that I loved her, that this was a wonderful thing.

I had always been a pacifier, a fixer, a person that does not panic, whatever the situation. I was on my game, it was working, she had stopped crying. I continued, cheering her up, telling her how great it was going to be, how much fun it would be, our new adventure, our exciting future.

Then in the middle of it all, after I was doing so well, after we were doing so well, I punched a hole in the kitchen door. It was a thin hardboard door, cheap and basic but it still took some doing, though that part of it seemed hard to remember, only seconds later. It was true though; the hole was there to prove it. I had just made a demanding situation much worse and what followed was an evening of great upset and anguish multiplied by my stupidity of destroying the kitchen door of someone that had been so incredibly kind to us. My initial calmness and positivity were replaced by panic and worry and, worst of all, the fact that, momentarily I had become the same as the person I despised the most. I had witnessed this exact thing many times during my childhood and far worse but letting myself, though fleetingly, be the same as him made me feel disgusted at myself for putting Megs in this position. I vowed to never let this happen again.

God, I loved her. I loved everything about her. The smile in her eyes, the smell of her hair, the way she laughed when others laughed and cried when they cried. Suddenly, life seemed pointless without her.

The next morning, I again tried to make it up to her, to make things right. I kissed her as she left quietly for work, and I was saddened to see the entire world on her shoulders. I walked straight to the do-it-yourself centre and bought a new door, primer, and paint. Within hours the door was hung, and the finishing coat had been applied.

I may not have been anyone that would have inspired confidence as a potential parent but when it came to building, fixing, and making anything then, for my age, I had few rivals.

That evening was better. With the door fixed and the evening meal painstakingly prepared by my own fair hands, together with a big bunch of flowers and a cheap bottle of sparkle, I set about trying to convince my lovely, clever, and hardworking girlfriend, and myself, that everything was going to be fine. There were a thousand problems with a million answers but the first and the biggest was simple. I had to get a job. A solid, well-paid job and I needed one quickly.
I upped my game in both seeking and applying for positions whilst spending my days packing batteries, assembling tool clamps, and making jerry cans in a machine shop. Weeks passed and not a single successful application. I spent every evening scouring the papers and magazines for an opportunity but to no avail.

Then, one day, something happened. Mr Wood happened.
I had on only a few occasions in my life, had something given to me on a plate. I have always been realistic enough that all the cliches are there for a reason. "You make your own luck," etc, etc.

I knew, however, that every now and then, if you keep your head down, work hard and never, ever give in to the bastards, then an opportunity will arise. I also knew that when something wonderful happens in life, there are more than several ways you can fuck it up.

I had met Mr Wood at my graduation show. I had assumed he was a senior lecturer of some kind or a big noise in one of the design journals that swooped down on degree shows every year, trying to spot the next design genius or laugh, secretly, at the complete shit some students had managed to regurgitate from previous students or famous names in design.

My show was not shit. It was incomplete, unpolished, and lacked the thoroughness of others, but the designs were original, brave even, perhaps too brave, but not shit.

He seemed a very exuberant character and was very striking in his white hair and fedora with his boating blazer, slacks and cravat. I had noticed that his glasses were "Armani," and these were the days before fake brands and replicas. The ensemble was completed with a cane, an old flexible, bamboo cane, reminiscent of Charlie Chaplin or Will Hay as a hapless schoolmaster. He had spent a great deal of time looking at a set of lamps I had designed and made from acrylic and concrete as well as a dining table that was in glass and concrete. I liked concrete. We had spent over an hour chatting and by the end of it he had said very complimentary things about my work. He had kindly taken one of my cards and as he left, I remember him saying, whilst looking at my details.

"Jeremiah, eh? I shall remember that name," then he was gone, straight towards the exit without a single glance to anyone else's display. Time plays tricks on one's memory, but if I picture him leaving the grand hall that day, nobody noticed him, even in his flamboyant splendour.

My Mam had called that evening, from the phone box.
I would be thirty-two years old by the time my brothers and I convinced her that she should have a phone line put in at home. She said I had received a letter marked urgent and did she want me to send it up or open it now. She did the latter and read out that I was requested to have an informal chat with Mr Wood to discuss a role in his company. There was a time and a place, and the last comment was that he, Mr Wood, was very much looking forward to seeing me again.

I thanked my extremely excited Mother and rang off. I could not wait to tell Megs, who had been excitedly sitting at my side praying for some, much needed, good news.

We were both over the moon and celebrated with sausage and chips and video from Blockbusters. I quickly phoned the number I had been given and confirmed that I would be attending the "chat". I had the weekend to prepare as the interview was on Monday.

After travelling down to Wales on the train on Sunday afternoon and staying with a college mate and resisting the temptation to have too many beers in our mini reunion, I found myself on the bus to Pontypool, the following morning, to the address. It was just a short walk from the bus stop to Visage Designs and what greeted me was a building that fell in line with the dozens of industrial buildings on the faceless trading estates I had spent my time in over the last few months in Banbury.

I must admit feeling a little unimpressed with the facade of the building, as the impression I had got from Mr Wood was that I was a golden ticket winner and had been invited to somewhere akin to "Willy Wonka Land."
The lady in reception was nice and I waited to be shown into my audience with Mr Wood, although there did not seem to be any other doors out of the reception apart from the door in and a door marked "Workshop."

Eventually, the lady asked me to follow her and with my portfolio under my arm I confusingly went with her outside into the open air again. "Keep following the building around and you will see a door, you cannot miss it. Ring the bell and Mr Wood will let you in. Good luck." She smiled sweetly and returned inside.

I did as was instructed and on the third side of the building I found the door, but it was not what I expected at all. It was huge, it was the sort of door you find on a large manor house. It was double-leafed and painted in navy blue, with enormous balustrades and Roman pillars to both sides.

It looked completely out of place on the otherwise bland exterior. There were topiary and boxed hedges immaculately manicured around the door and mat on the doorstep that read "Dare to Dream." There was a large, brass vertical doorbell with a brass double ended llama embossed on the handle. I knew the image from the film "Dr Dolittle" with one of my favourite childhood actors, Rex Harrison. I searched for its name and my rather peculiar memory kindly provided me with "Push me Pull me," the name of the species of animal from the film. "That is very cool," I decided, as I pushed and pulled at the doorbell in and out instead of the more natural motion of up and down. There was a delay then very loudly indeed through what seemed a crackly tannoy, of the type used in a 1970's holiday camp, came a song I recognised, "Happy days are here again."

There was then a sound of a huge gong, reminiscent of the muscular fella from the "Arthur Rank Organisation," and the doors opened inwards without any assistance from anybody whatsoever.
Strangely I did not seem perturbed by this unusual turn of events, but I was enjoying every moment. I boldly walked into the large foyer which, to my obsessive eye for detail, was a pastiche of a curved staircase found in large stately homes or even a grand theatre. Fake though it was, it was a bloody good one, with finials and Art Nouveau detailing. I recognised copies of Galle and Lalique's work in the beautifully made simulation. I had coincidentally done my third-year dissertation on the history of glass and was, for a brief time, relatively knowledgeable on the subject. To the left and to the right of the staircase were two doors. The one on the left had a hand painted sign on it that read "Fame and Fortune," the other said simply "Happiness." This was a quite simple choice, surely.

If this was a test of one's integrity and forward thinking, then surely happiness would be the choice over fame and fortune.

One's happiness could indeed contain fame and fortune, but fame and fortune did not necessarily contain happiness. Happiness, for anyone, must be the goal. That surely was the right door to choose. I quickly approached the right-hand door, even outstretching my hand to turn the knob. Then, something stopped me.

I noticed that the door went all the way to the floor unlike the other which had a gap. Also, there were no visible hinges on the door and no gaps on the sides or above.

It was, rather deceptively another hoax and I also noticed, upon closer inspection a small spring on the door handle that may have been a crude detection device. The door also felt cold like it was against a brick wall. I inspected the door to the left, it was warm, like the room beyond was occupied, heated even. The hinges were in place and, without any reason to suspect otherwise, was indeed a working, common or garden door. I had wasted enough time deliberating and was conscious of keeping Mr Wood waiting. I firmly grabbed the handle, turned it confidently and entered.

I watched as the sign that said, "Fame and Fortune" revolved automatically like an old-fashioned mobile blackboard to settle at "Happiness." I turned to see the other door do the exact same thing but in complete reverse. I was certain that I had made the right choice. The room I had entered was enormous for what it was, I assumed, intended to be. The walls were draped with silks and satins in swathes and bows, as was the ceiling. It had no discernible windows, but much of the light came from a gigantic chandelier that hung in the centre of the ceiling where the pleats of the fabric all gathered. On the walls were Renaissance style paintings with ornate gold frames all lit with a designated lamp curved over the top. The furniture, to me, seemed to be French and the name Louis the Fourteenth screamed out at me from my limited knowledge of such things. There were chaise lounges, bureaus, chairs and tables with lamps and clocks and large vases with ornaments adorning every corner and available space.

The floor was covered with rugs of, what seemed, the finest silks and golden threads and at the end of the room was a rather elegant desk with ball and claw feet and golden lion heads beneath an ornate green and cream onyx top. Next to the desk was a large, three panelled changing screens with roman gods and serving girls embroidered on every inch.

As if by magic or as if someone had shouted "Action!" Mr Wood appeared from behind the screens.

"Ahh, Jeremiah, I am so pleased you managed to pass my little test. Believe me, I've had them standing out there for hours," he announced in his, now familiar, rather grand accent with just a hint of his Welsh origins. "Are you well?" I relaxed instantly.

"I am very well, Mr Wood, and hope you are too. Lovely to see you again." For some reason, I sounded posher. I would have to keep this in check. I always picked up the way people spoke very quickly and subconsciously, which changed the way I spoke. There is a fine line between this being a compliment and taking the piss, which was almost never my intention.

"Yes, wonderful to see you again dear boy and thank you for coming to see me. I bet you are wondering what this is all about, are you not?" He said as he turned up his performance, ever so slightly. Mr Wood was wearing a full-length smoking jacket in diamond padded fabric, weaved in greens and golds with what closely resembled peacocks embroidered throughout. The large collars and cuffs were in a contrasting burgundy velvet. On his head was a matching hat with a tassel that I had never seen anyone wear before or since, apart from Uncle Bulgaria from "The Wombles." His presentation was finished with his trademark cravat, this time in vibrant orange. I could not see his feet, but I completed the entire look in my head with a pair of golden silk slippers that curled at the toes, that could well have been a gift from Yul Brynner from "The King and I." I took a moment to revel in what a wondrous moment this was. I had craved unique moments in my life and eccentric people. Here I was experiencing both. I was no longer on a trading estate in Pontypool but a Bedouin tent in Arabia or a magisterial palace in a far-flung Chinese province.

"Yes, it is true, Mr Wood. I have been curious." I had found my level now, interesting, and polite with perfect diction. "Excellent, excellent," he exclaimed, clapping his hands excitedly. "Well, as you know, I am a huge fan of your work."

"I'm afraid the University took a slightly different view," I said solemnly, hoping that honesty was the best policy.

He became rather animated. "What the fuck do they know? They could not spot topaz in a tub of toenails. Now you listen to me Jeremiah. I know a gift when I see one and yours has only been hampered by the three years you have spent at that God awful place. It is about communication and style. It is about arrogance and humility. You have it, they do not. They hand out their medals of mediocrity after knocking out any originality and truth of thought. I know, better than anyone, you cannot spend a fucking medal." Upon which, he opened an ornate box in mother of pearl and walnut on his desk and took out a cigarette and a long ebony cigarette holder, married the two and lit the end with a large, unnecessarily heavy, lighter in gold and crystal on his desk. He then puffed an enormous plume of smoke into the air and seemed to wait for the applause.

I refrained from cheering his monologue but in my head, there was an eruption, the type of reaction that I had only heard on the completion of championship point at Wimbledon or following the final crescendo at the "Last Night of the Proms".

"Thank you, Mr Wood, I don't know what to say." I did not.
"Well, how about this? You come and work for me as a project leader. We have a large contract with Harrods in Knightsbridge. We must transform their window displays on the ground floor, ready for Christmas, forty-two in all and design and build them a Santa's Grotto, the likes of which London has never seen before. This must all be completed and installed by the middle of November.

You will start next Monday and for your time and talent I will pay you £24,000.00 per year." He tilted his head back and again released another plume of cyclonic smoke.

I heard the words Harrods, Santa and £24,000.00 per year. I nearly burst, almost jumped around the room, and very nearly rushed up to him and tackled an embrace, ripping the cigarette holder from his grasp and having a large, show stopping puff myself. "That would be most agreeable Mr Wood," I smiled, barely staying in character.

"Good show, Jeremiah, now if you could excuse me, I have a portrait to paint of some bloody Duchess. Give your details to Cressida at the front desk and we will see you on Monday." Taking his last drag and poking his cigarette into what might have served well as a fruit bowl. "I will, Mr Wood, Cressida, ahh yes," I said earnestly, though I knew her name to be Julie. "And thank you, you have no idea what this means to me."
Mr Wood wiggled the four fingers of his right hand in response and disappeared behind the screens. I guessed he would have to stay there until I left so I did so as quickly as I could.

Back on the train back to Banbury, I must have looked like some deranged buffoon with the biggest smile on my face. I had called Megs from the station, and she had squealed with delight. We had never dared to believe things could work out so well and we quickly planned that I would stay with my pal then look for a flat whilst she worked up to a month before her due date, which was mid-May, then join me in Newport, were we had gone to university nearby. My salary of £24,000.00 per year was an unbelievable amount of money to earn for my first job out of university, bearing in mind that a newly qualified teacher's starting salary for the time was £17,000.00 or the fact that my stepfather had never earned more than £350.00 per week, as a roofer, though we had seen very little of that.

Auntie Barbie once again came up trumps by gifting us her old Peugeot that we nicknamed "The Pig," because of its faded red paintwork that now looked very much like a sunburned sow. We were ready to start a whole new adventure.

I started on the following Monday and loved the job instantly. I was given a team of six people who all seemed great apart from an older guy called Karl who had a ridiculous moustache and called me a "college boy," at our first team meeting.

When I said, "You can cut that shit out Tom fucking Selleck," he thankfully smiled, happy with his new moniker. I am glad I didn't say "Ron fucking Jeremy," which had been my first thought. The work was amazing.

My team were working on "special" projects whilst the rest of the factory completed the main contract which was to convince Christmas shoppers at Harrods that a two thirds scale replica of "The Mallard," a steam train from the 1930's that was an icon both of engineering and classic design, was travelling the world picking up Christmas gifts from every country on the globe, ready for the big day.

Each of the forty-two windows was to be a station from a different country reflecting the wonderful diversity of nations and cultures. Spices from India, silks from the Middle East and teas from China etc. There was a Pullman's carriage in each window, all sign-written and coach built to match exactly the original, only one third smaller.

My projects included a nine-foot diameter acrylic swimming pool with animatronic polar bears in scuba gear swimming below and on the surface of the pool, a gigantic animatronic whale with moving tail and fibre optic waterspout and animated mouth and an enormous snow globe with constant snow falling inside made from polystyrene beads, a sewer pipe with holes in it and a vacuum pump.

We also had two emergency jobs in which we had to paint forty glass fibre fake pig carcasses to look like the real thing for the food halls inside the most famous shop in the world and a hundred huge imitation candles that were made from plastic drainpipes, bunged at one end, sprayed white and dipped into molten wax until they looked like real candles. The effect was completed by dripping wax down the length of the candle and putting a small, flickering filament in the top.

I was absolutely in my element; I loved the challenge and the instant satisfaction of designing and making as one continuous process. I was always first at the factory at seven o'clock and found myself the last to leave twelve hours later. I worked weekends and was so engrossed in the work that I had to remind myself to eat and take a toilet break. I only saw Mr Wood on a few occasions which was always later in the evening when only I remained. He was continually complimentary of my work, and the fact that my team was motivated by the fact I led by example and did not expect them to do anything that I was not prepared to do. On one memorable evening, after sharing with me a bottle of Moet & Chandon, he pulled away in his bright yellow Rolls Royce, which he had driven into the centre of the factory, in the space left by the engine of The Mallard, which was now installed at Harrods but, as yet, hidden from the public. He rolled the window down and held his cane out like a horse backed hero at the "Charge of the Light Brigade."

"Together, Jeremiah, we will rule the world." Life was good.

I had managed to find a spacious flat above "Shop-a-Check," on Chepstow Road in Newport. It was large and clean but had no heating whatsoever. A few gas heaters later and the problem was solved. I furnished the place with the help of The Salvation Army and tried desperately to pretend that the bloke upstairs was not a serial killer. Megs visited on the weekends and travelled down from Oxfordshire in her newly acquired yellow Beetle which, ironically, also had no heating.

By the time she got to Wales, the hot water bottle that Auntie Barb had strapped to her tummy with a scarf, was almost cold. She loved the flat and it became a happy place where we first had set up our first proper home. We planned for the baby, and I even decorated one of the bedrooms as a nursery.

I had looked at many flats before finding this one, on the rare days I was off. One sticks in my mind which really was unsuitable. The estate agent had indeed promised a nursery that was already decorated with "Thomas the Tank Engine" wallpaper. He showed me into the promised room with excitement.

"That's really nice mate," I said sarcastically, surveying the walls. "It's a shame about the spelling though," "Fuck oof Pigs," was spray painted in red on the main wall, just below Thomas' smiling face, who clearly enjoyed the handiwork of the ill-educated graffiti artist more than I.

The work at the factory was finished. Everything had been transported to a holding area underneath the world-famous store. I was to spend the next eight weeks supervising and installing all the work we had so painstakingly crafted.

Missing the deadline was not an option and it was made clear by the powers that be that the success of this operation was particularly important to the financial future of the company.

I travelled down the next Sunday night and checked into our digs, just outside Knightsbridge.
The hotel was a grand old affair that would have once been an impressive part of the London scene but was now a very tired and sad memory of its former self, full of dusty chandeliers and faded drapes, worn stair carpets and ill-fitting doors. The breakfast, the next morning however, was splendid in both quality and portion size.

It would be twelve hours before I would eat again so I feasted like a housebound obesity patient whose ambulance was minutes away from taking him to get a gastric band fitted.

Harrods was incredible. The bustle and the hustle of everyone around. The aroma of privilege coexisting only feet away from the easily ignored stench of the unloved. The grandeur of the interiors, the wealth, the unashamed gluttony of the poverty exempt washed over me as I excitedly bathed in the well of success, knowing that at any moment the whistle would blow and I would be sent scurrying back over the fence, to the world of the unwashed.

My overbearing thoughts were of the difference between what the customers saw and what was behind the scenes. The disorder and chaos, the dirt, and the disbelief. Entering from the loading bay was like reading a book from the last page backwards. All the secrets were revealed yet the reason for those secrets were, so far, unimportant. The area where we were to start installing our displays was shut off to the public and so we set to work in making the dreams we had collectively formed into a reality. The work was long and hard. The carrying, the manoeuvring, the fixing and finishing all stole time from our schedule but the unerring sense of duty and excitement drove us all on.

Glitches and changes were dealt with daily and eventually, after several weeks the site started to look somewhere near what we had envisaged in the months previous. As our deadline approached, I started to feel that although everything was now in place and everything was working mechanically the way it should have been, everything lacked a certain magic. I could not put my finger on it, and everyone in charge at the store seemed delighted, but I felt a little uneasy. I should not have worried. No one had told me about Andre.

"Socks on your cocks and bums against the walls boys, Andre is here and ready to be fabulous."

That was my first introduction to Andre. He just marched into our display area at the end of a particularly long shift where we were removing any debris and cleaning the site ready for handover. "Now, which of you love trumpets is Lyndon? Lyndon, L-y-n-d-o-n come out you cheeky boy." I stood in complete and utter shock, unprepared for what was now happening. I had never in my life met anyone quite like Andre before. I had met gay fellas before, of course, at university who it was clear were camp. I had even talked the subject over with a house mate of mine called Andy, who had confided in me that he was on the verge of telling his parents he was gay. Andy's biggest issue was that he was a six-foot Sunderland lad with a deep voice and not an inkling of the secret he was keeping was visible to the outside world. Breaking it to his Mam would be easy. His Dad, who was a lifelong miner, on the other hand, would prove far more heart-breaking for the whole family.

Andy took his own life a few years later using a car exhaust and a length of hosepipe. It is something that haunts me still. If only I could have introduced Andy to Andre.

"Umm, I'm Lyndon," I said, unconvincingly. "Oh, aren't you a sight for a sore arse. Mr Wood said you would debrief me. Aren't I a lucky girl?" Andre was very tall, very black and had the biggest mouth I had ever seen. He was resplendent with a large afro hairstyle, crowned with an oversized purple fedora.

He had a bright green silk shirt with at least some of the buttons done up, with black satin flared sailor bag trousers covering most of his silver platform shoes.

He had bangles, beads, and chains and about everything it was possible to hang off one's body. He was, in a word, magnificent. Never had anyone made a first impression on me like he did that day.

I knew myself well enough to know that I was already obsessed with this strange alien character and that I would have to, very quickly, become a little more fabulous myself in his presence to avoid being completely shaded by his luminescence. "You are, indeed, Andre, pleased to meet you. How can I help?" I held out my hand in welcome. "Let's skip the formalities, Darling, you may kiss my ring," he held out his hand which had an enormous fake ruby ring on it. I felt that this was a test. I saw Karl's face in the corner of my eye, his Magnum P.I. tache was doing the Cha-Cha-Cha. I walked towards Andre and took his hand in mine and theatrically kissed the ring. "Welcome, Your Majesty," I announced like a master of ceremony.

"Oooh," Andre squealed and clapped with delight. "We are going to have such fun, now let us get these boys off to a hot bath and I will tell you exactly what I'll need. Go on off you toddle and do not forget the three F's. Face, feet and fanny." The room cleared like a fire drill headed by Karl, whose head and shoulders twitched like a scarecrow in a gale.

"Firstly, I am going to call you London, because it suits you and we will hear no more about it," he said, matter-of-factly. "London it is then," I said, laughing loudly. Andre then took a small bottle of vodka and two small, elegant cut glasses from his bag and we sat on some packing crates and talked effortlessly for a few hours about a high-profile footballer he was seeing, a member of the House of Lords he had sex with in a Taxi, and the night he had danced with Freddie Mercury. I could have listened all night but eventually lack of food and sleep forced me to bid him farewell.
"Thanks for listening, London," he smiled, taking my hand and kissing it on the back.
"Goodnight, Your Majesty," I smiled.
It seemed only a matter of hours before I was back on site the next morning. I was first to arrive and what greeted me was an amazing and unforgettable vision.

The entire place was no longer a building site or a collection of unrelated displays but a pure wonderland of dreams and imagination. Andre, it turned out, was the most sought-after window dresser in the capital and what he had produced in a few short hours was nothing short of miraculous. Using fake snow, lights, electric candles, glass jewels of every possible colour, beads, pearls, draped satins, and crinolines he had transformed our designs into the most perfect wonderland imaginable.

I turned on the main electrical circuit to give the full effect. The animated polar bears burst into life, as did the enormous whale with its multicoloured waterspout and the huge snow globe with Victorian backdrop and endless winter snowfall. The music also kicked in on the loop with children's choral voices singing endlessly and with heart-bursting charm. I sat and just watched. I had never been so proud of anything in my life, I was lost in the moment, lost in Christmas and the Christmases to come with Megs and the baby for the rest of our happy lives. I noticed a note pinned to a backdrop, it simply read.

"My dearest London, your ever dutiful Queen. Andre x"

A gentleman entered the room in a pinstripe suit. He was short and middle eastern looking. His clothes looked awfully expensive, and he walked with his hands behind his back.

I assumed him to be part of Harrods security as he exuded an air of authority or at least a given right to be there. He examined everything in minute detail, taking much joy in its performance and effectiveness. He greeted me with a quiet "Hello," and continued to enjoy the scene. I smiled and busied myself with very little. After a few moments or so he approached me and shook my hand. "This is all very good, thank you," he spoke in a rich Arabian accent. He then reached into his suit pocket and gave me something. "This is for you, thank you once again."

He then hurriedly continued along the display, through the curtain and disappeared from view. A "Thank you," seemed simple and appropriate. I looked at what he had given me, and it was a crisp fifty-pound note, blemish free and perfect. It sat in my hand like an imposter, a crazed night of debauched drink or a week's rent. I found out later that day that the gentleman I met was Mr Al Fayed, the owner of Harrods.

He seemed genuinely nice.

Our display was now complete and after getting the project signed off and locked up in preparation for the Christmas period, I was given the rather shocking news that Luke, the factory foreman had been involved in an accident in the workshop whilst he was putting the finishing touches to the last few carriages on the Mallard display. Somebody had reckoned it a clever idea to stack some sheets of 18mm MDF on their ends against a wall. When the shutter door was opened the wind got behind one of the sheets and blew it over.

The story goes that Luke was standing close, unaware of the danger. The sheet fell forward and came down on him, narrowly missing his head, with the sharp edge but catching his ear, which it efficiently removed, almost entirely, in an enormous guillotine action and was held on only by its lobe. He was now in the hands of a plastic surgeon at Newport/Gwent Hospital and would not be returning to work at least until the new year. Luke was a great guy and I had learned a great deal from him, but this was not good news for the schedule as he would have overseen completing the contract to the deadline. I spent the rest of the day looking around the main display on the ground floor windows. It was starting to look incredible but there was still much to do before it could be handed over to Andre and his team to make the real magic happen. It was so satisfying to see a project that so many of us had worked on for so long become a reality due to our hard work and commitment.

All hands were on deck and even some of the staff from the office had been called in to fetch and carry. I recognised Jayne from accounts as she walked towards me, smiling and happy to have a few days staying in London for work, something that was a rare treat.

"Hi Lyndon, Mr Wood would like to see you and asked if you could take these brushes over for him too. Here is the address, it is only a few streets away," she handed me a slip of paper and three, brand new brushes of differing sizes, the type you use for painting portraits and landscapes and scurried away excitedly, safe in the knowledge there would not be a single spreadsheet on her horizon today. I was pleased to get the message as it would be good to see Mr Wood again. I had not seen him in nearly two months since I was back at the factory.

Also, I strongly suspected that he wanted to see me regarding covering for Luke whilst he was recovering from his accident. I had a vague idea of where I was going as I made my way out of the store into the unrelenting throng that was the early Christmas shoppers, quickly moving off the main street and down a side road.

I instantly spotted the road name of the address and followed it along until I found the handsome Georgian frontage of an old townhouse property that was now six, incredibly small but no doubt expensive apartments.
I found the intercom, checked the number, and pressed the corresponding button, moving my head close to the receiver, expecting to speak to Mr Wood before entry. I was a little surprised to be buzzed through straight away and so I put my shoulder to the heavy door and was immediately in a small foyer and heading up the two flights of stairs to the number of the apartment on the address, the three brushes still gripped in my hand.

I was in the highest of moods as I confidently knocked the door, knowing that Mr Wood's gamble on me had paid dividends and I was extremely proud that I was able to repay his faith in me by playing a significant part in making the Harrods project a complete success. Life was good.

I thought that I had become quite accustomed to Mr Wood's, let's say, unique sartorial elegance but even I was a little taken aback by what greeted me as he opened the deeply panelled oak door.

"Come in Jeremiah. Welcome to my little lair, away from the lunacy of London life." a phrase I had no doubt had been used many times before. Mr Wood was wearing an expensive looking Japanese kimono. It was emblazoned with Dragons and Samurai in the full flow of battle. It instantly reminded me of an off-duty Inspector Clouseau relaxing in his bijou, Paris apartment. The phrase "Not now, Cato," ninjaed momentarily on my lips but remained silently out of sight, rather like Cato himself. Mr Wood's oriental night attire struck me as being a little shorter than I would have imagined comfortable, and its meagre length seemed accentuated by his cotton white, biro-blue veined turkey legs and gold monogrammed slippers.

"Hello, Mr Wood," I replied with genuine positivity, "I've brought the brushes you asked for." I held them out for him to see but kept them in my hand as everywhere looked so neat and tidy that I didn't know where to put them down.
"Brushes, what brushes? Ahh yes, the brushes, that is right, the brushes, thank you. Jeremiah, I have been meaning to catch up with you for a while now, but as you can tell things have been very busy and I haven't had a moment. I so appreciate the hard work you have been putting in and thanks to you and the rest of the team, we are close to completing our biggest contract to date. The client is delighted and so am I. Well done, young man, well done."

I was so incredibly proud of myself. I had an issue with praise, I had known it for years. I had craved it as a child, not from females, I had that covered, but from men. Men the age of a dad or a grandad. Men who could acknowledge my existence, who could validate my worthiness.

I could never take a compliment from anyone without dismissing it with a throwaway remark, a joke or a distracting comment. This one, from Mr Wood, I took. I drank it down in one. I swung it round my head like a microphone held by a Tom Jones impersonator during his last song on a Saturday night at the club. I deserved it, I had earned it, he was right. I was a fucking hero.

Mr Wood interrupted my Walter Mitty moment. "I would like you to take over, temporarily, from Luke. After his unfortunate accident we are going to need someone with your talents to see us over the line with this one and you, Jeremiah, are that man." More praise, more adulation.
It washed over me like a bucket of golden frogspawn. More, Mr Wood, more.

"I would not expect you to do this for nothing, of course, your salary would increase. I would pay you thirty thousand a year and the position would come with a company vehicle.

Luke will not need his whilst he is recovering, and this would give you the opportunity to shine." My Head was spinning, my insides were convulsing like it was a first date, could this day get any better? I could have kissed the old bastard. Upon reflection, I am glad I didn't.

I spoke for the first time in a while since my life had irrevocably changed. "I don't know what to say Mr Wood, that would be wonderful, thank you," I said with a humility reminiscent of a one-off Oscar winner, convinced they would be the greatest of all time.

I was delighted and my overbearing thought was to tell Megs. Our future was secure, I could provide, we were going to be ok. Mr Wood smiled the smile I had seen a hundred times. Pleased for my success, proud to have discovered such a talent. Then he said, "Before we sort out the details, however, I would like to introduce you to someone." My gormless smile and relentless nodding continued as the last statement filtered through my smugness resulting in the breaking news headline flashing across my subconscious. "Wait, what now? What did he say? Pardon. Meet someone? Was there someone else in the flat?"

I scanned the space, looking at the doorways of all the rooms, of which there were only two, that exited the main living area into a bedroom and, I guessed, a bathroom.

Who was going to enter the room? His legal representative to arrange the contract? Mister Al Fayed to celebrate my glorious life? Shirley Bassey singing 'Goldfinger'? My eyes finally fixed back on Mr Wood, my expression was one of confusion, of a loss of thread, my eyes narrowed as if to say, "I don't know what you mean."

His, same but different, smile was mirrored by my own as our eyes looked straight at each other. I waited for him to speak but he did not. Then he slowly broke my gaze and his eyes started to descend, followed seconds later by his head. I was laser locked onto the same course and I too started to follow with my eyes to where he was leading me. Eventually we were looking at his feet, I checked his slippers, they were still hideous. "Why is he looking at his slippers?" I thought to myself. Then there was a movement, almost unnoticeable at first, behind the Japanese kimono. The movement became a bulge.

It started to rise until slowly and unmistakably it revealed itself for both of us to see, casting aside firstly one silky curtain, then the other until it nodded its appearance, encouraged by the instant release of the weight of its confines.

This seemed to encourage it somewhat and it continued to grow and swell in my direction until this one-eyed monster was aimed directly at an approximate angle of forty-five degrees, at my forehead. If a bullet had shot out of the end of it, killing me instantly, at that point in time, I would have been neither surprised nor disappointed in the conclusion of the slow-motion scenario. Mr Wood looked upwards with, what I presumed was, a seductive, suck my dick, smile.

The reason I presumed this was because I did not look at his face. I looked slightly over his shoulder at a large, ornate, golden framed mirror on the wall and caught my own reflection.
Looking back at me was Eric Morecambe, or at least his expression, the one that he used to "look to camera" mid comedy sketch, when he and the TV audience realised the reality of the situation. The only massive difference was that there was no laughter. This was not a moment of levity.

"Oh, for fuck's sake. Really? This was what it was? This whole episode in my life, the success, the self-respect, my joyous U-turn of fortune was all a sham?" I continued my nanosecond, inside voice, conversation with myself in the mirror.

So, I was not a great designer, I had not impressed and excelled and deserved and warranted the success? My life had not changed. I was not the proud provider of warmth and security for Megs and the baby after all.

I was just a young, naive, hoodwinked boy from a council estate with a warm smile and here I was in a room with the expectation upon me to wank off an old man, or worse, for money or a job or a car or a down payment on a flat or the love and respect of my family. "Oh bollocks, really?" Time had frozen, I was acutely aware of my surroundings, Mr Wood stood still, the excitement of his pending penis party still smeared on his face.

I did not actually despise him for it, he had not really committed a crime, this wasn't illegal. I was twenty-one, hardly an abused teenager.

Yes, he had used his power and position to manipulate and coerce me into what he hoped was a jolly good noshing, but I was not stupid enough not to realise this sort of thing happened all the time. Don't get me wrong, the thought never entered my mind to go anywhere near his wrinkly old todger, but I did feel sorry for him in a way. Was his only way of finding affection to manufacture a situation like this? Was I the first? Clearly not.

The sleekness of his delivery told me that. Would there be others? Of course, there would. Well, maybe, I could make sure he would think twice about taking this stroll along the 'Phallisade' again.

You see, Mr Wood had made a big mistake that day, he had made assumptions, lots of them. He had assumed because I spoke nicely and was constantly effervescent that I was shallow as a stream, that I was from a nice, middle-class background, with holidays and car rides and a matching duvet set on my bed. He did not know about the weekly beatings from a drunken stepfather, the years of not knowing my own father. The nights of planning my revenge, the kid in his bedroom with anger and fire in his belly. My revenge was never to be violent; I was sick of that. It was to be smart, clever, concise, and contrived. I would be the hero of my own story; I would show my stepfather that I was a better man than he.

I was an odd child in many ways.

He had no idea of the scrapes I had been in, the thinking on my feet to get out of them. He was unaware of our forthcoming addition to our family; the protective instinct mother nature injects you with at such times.

All he saw was a pretty, little valley boy with an obliging smile and an undoubtedly tight sphincter. He could also never be aware of the voice in my head, quiet at first, a whisper really. It was Charlie's voice. It was always Charlie's voice. Whenever I was in a position of crisis. Whenever I had an outrageous thought in my head like a man bending over in the street, tying his shoelaces. In my head was Charlie. "Go on Lynd, kick him up the arse." Here was Charlie again, louder now. "Go on Lynd, teach this dirty old fucker a lesson."

I fought the impulse, I really did. The thought forming in my head would be devastating. It would change things irreversibly for the bad. Gone would be the job, the security and looming would be the difficult, nye on impossible, conversation with Megs on how I had, with one moment of madness caused our house of cards to come tumbling down that was, moments before, made of the finest bricks and mortar. "Go on Lynd," laughed Charlie. Back in the moment and back to the stare of Mr Wood who was smiling with his top lip only, revealing his immaculate dentures and his perverted line of thought.
I composed myself. Looking directly at Mr Wood's erection I said in my best parlour voice. "Hello there, little fella, you are a handsome boyo aren't you." Bending down and on to my knees I continued. "I bet you would love a little tickle with my special love brush wouldn't you." I nearly vomited when his knob actually nodded. "Yessss please," said Mr Wood breathlessly.

"Quiet now," I said to Mr Wood, holding up the single, largest brush in chastisement. The other two were discarded to the floor.

"Ooooh!" said Mr Wood, his old boy, dancing like a spring lamb. This was the first time I became aware of his wrinkly, low swinging testicles, his clock weights, his onion bag, his two walnuts in a pop sock.

228

They were grotesque and swung side to side like a withered metronome counting down the moments until their crinkled crescendo. I felt the brush in my hand, I could feel the springiness of the beech. I could sense the potential energy in its bend as I flexed it with my thumbs. "You will enjoy this Mr Wood, brace yourself," I teased, like a two-bit harlot.

Mr Wood closed his eyes and lifted his head to the heavens. He was quivering and I sensed there was a matter of urgency before the unthinkable happened. "Go on, Lynd," Charlie chuckled, impatiently. With that, I firmly held the metal ferrule of the handle and the soft bristles in one hand and curved the handle close to breaking point with the other then released it onto his ballbag. There was a sound far louder than I had expected. It was a ballseye, cock on. The thwack was extraordinary, like the slapping of a water filled carrier bag. I immediately stood up and back, this was the bit I was not in control of. His reaction was instant and cataclysmic. The sound he made was extremely hard to describe. It was animalistic in origin with elements of a dented steam kettle. I heard seagulls and rusty gates and factory hooters and air raid sirens contrasting with cellos and bellows and fat opera fellows. It was high, it was low, it was fast, it was slow. He breathed in, he breathed out, in whisper and shout. He bobbed and he sobbed, he flailed and he wailed. He blinked and winked, he sighed and he cried and held onto his balls that were aching inside.
I can only apologise for my divergence into verse, but the scene was truly theatrical and went beyond the real world into a realm reminiscent of "The Nutcracker Suite."

Mr Wood made some of the strangest noises I had ever heard, and his footwork was spectacular too. He tranced and pranced and "River Danced." He cradled his nut sack like his faithful old dog had been a recent roadkill victim and he equally lamented its demise.

I gathered the other two brushes from the floor (I was nothing if not neat) and placed all three in a small, elegant, cut-glass vase on the side table. I then straightened a cushion on a side chair with the thoroughness of an assassin re-adjusting the scene.

Mr Wood was now poleaxed on an ornate chaise lounge, one hand on his ageing love spuds and the other, palm upwards, on his forehead, like a lovestruck silent movie starlet needing to pee. His breathing reminded me of the sow I once aided, in a difficult birth, on Windy Hill Farm. "Thank you, Mr Wood, for all you've done for me. I really do appreciate it," I said calmly, meaning every word, and moving toward the door. "I'm sorry things didn't work out, Jeremiah," said Mr Wood, an octave higher than I recognised. "Bless him," I reminisced in thought. I smiled and turned the door handle to leave.

"One more thing," he said breathlessly. I turned. "Could you at least finish me off before you leave?"

Mr Wood's wood was back. Charlie and I laughed long and loud as I left the apartment.

Life was good.

The Eulogy of Keith Charles Thomas

(Charlie)

Saturday November 5th

2023

Funeral Service

at

Margam Crematorium

It was a day for death.

It had been weeks since I'd received the news about Charlie on a cold, concrete staircase that echoed my breathless questions across three floors to all who didn't care, who had rejoiced in the news that it wasn't them today. He was fifty-three years old. Tear-soaked arrangements had been made by those strong enough to cope. A time slot had been booked at the crematorium and at the pub afterwards. Money had changed hands.

My Dad did not do death.

He was with me today though; he knew it was important to me. I had given him no choice. I had stayed at his flat the night before, his excuse had hovered on his lips a few times, but in a life where I had endlessly accepted his shortcomings, he knew not to test me. I was proud of the way he had begrudgingly scrubbed up. The steam scrummaged down the blackened, brackened hills of Port Talbot as we made our way to the Crem.

The rain beat down like Noah's piss, St Petering off conveniently as we passed through the burley gates and up the long, larch lined drive. Long and lost faces I was pleased to see and were pleased to see me nodded in muted acknowledgement as we queued under the ribbed concrete tunnel to the entrance.

My Dad did not do polite conversation.

A pasty, little woman, oozing stupidity from every make-up clogged pore of her overfed face performed to whoever would listen, trying unsuccessfully to big up her part with the mock shock of her brief grief. "I'd go to her fucking funeral," said my Dad, without a hint of a whisper. It provided a much-needed levity, contrasting to the darkness of the day. We stood next to Big Ken, John Tarw and a few other Neath legends who had long since reached the brow of the hill but still basked, as we all did, in the reflective glow of our pasts. My mind flitted to a morning after the night before some three years previous. Charlie and I had been out on what he liked to call "manoeuvres" one Sunday lunchtime, a huge treat for me, another day at the office for him. The years had fallen away as we had laughed and coaxed the absolute best out of each other.

After consuming five pints each, he had broken off and ordered a pint on the side as my pace slowed, this continued for three more rounds until he was drinking three to my one, each golden thimble seemed to disappear in minutes in his huge hands accompanied by two roll ups to every glass. I had helped him from the taxi that evening and settled him into the sleep off zone in his monstrous reclining armchair before finding a drunken solace, myself, in his bedroom upstairs.

You'll be dead in two years, if you carry on like this, you dickhead," I had scolded the next morning.

"Fuck off, book boy," he had gravelled in retort, releasing the spray from the opening of a can of lager in my direction with impeccable timing. He had chosen that name because he knew it was a touchpaper slur from our past. He also knew that it was now worn as a badge of honour.

Who was I to hand out such advice? Was I someone qualified to cast the first stone? We both knew I was not. God, I missed him.

I had bullied my way into speaking that day. I had spoken to Bomber, Charlie's Dad and Ben, his son. I had made up some bollocks about a pact we had both made, a promise to give each other a send-off to be remembered. I had made it clear that it meant a great deal to me, and it did. There was no such agreement, no blood brother slicing of thumbs. Despite my hungover warning, I thought he was indestructible. The truth was I did not trust anyone else to do it, to fuck it up, to fumble over ill-chosen stories of drunkenness and excess. He was more than that, he was magnificent, and I alone could bang that gong for all to hear.

There were those in the Chapel of Rest that day that hated the very sight of me, that longed to scratch my eyes out or to kick my lifeless body around a pub car park. To twist the heel of their shoe into my throat. I loved that. Charlie would have thrived on it. Today was not for the faint of heart.

Seated with the order of service in my hand, refusing to look down at it in fear of seeing a picture of Charlie that would destroy my resolve, turning me into the dishevelled, weepy-eyed, high-pitched buffoon that lay paper thin below the surface.

My Dad did not do public expressions of emotion.

He sat to my left, his head twitching side to side, sensing my nerves but unable to comfort me.

Reading. Hymn. Poem. Hymn.

My name was read out and I was invited up to say a few words. I walked to the lectern, avoiding the screen above that I knew was showing pictures of him. "Oi, Lynd," he beckoned. "Fuck off, Charles," I replied to the bewilderment of the nonreligious minister, who visibly winced at what he assumed was a bad booking. At the pulpit I steadied myself, looked around the Chapel. It was packed to the rafters. I could see through the windows that there was a huge crowd of people outside. The microphone feedback created a much-needed pause, I noticed a second's delay from the echo on the tannoy outside of the Chapel. Deep breath.

"Don't fuck this up, book boy," whispered Charlie. I began...

"Let me start by telling you something that you already know. There will never, ever, EVER be anyone quite like Keith Charles Thomas. Forget about "breaking the mould", there was no mould. He was unique, a one off. The word legend is overused these days, but the word could have been created just for him. In another life he could have been an entrepreneur, an international rugby player or heavyweight champion of the world. If born in a different century, he could have been Owain Glyndwr."

I turned to the coffin; I needed his approval.

"How is that for an opening, Charlie? All right?

He would laugh if he heard me talking about him in this way. "Still full of shit then, Lynd," he would say. And I am, it's true. I am full of shit. But that was because of him.

Charlie was my best friend. But I was not his.

"You were." It was Charlie's voice, loud and clear in my head. "Not now, Charlie, not today, you swine," I thought. I heard him laugh. Deep breath, then I stumbled back in.

Well, I was but Charlie had hundreds of best friends and I am so pleased to see them all here today. On a day like this, quite naturally, I suppose, we look for positives to hold onto, to comfort us in our time of bereavement. Positives that ease the pain of losing someone so cherished by us all. As I look around this Chapel of Rest today and see all the faces that Charlie held so dear, who spent time in his company and were a daily part of his work and recreation, I can think of only one.

Because you are all here today, to remember Charlie, Neath Police have been given the morning off. It's what they describe as a quiet shift.

Oh! That was very daring of you, but I think you got away with it," delighted Charlie.

I first met Charlie when he was eight years of age, when I was ten. The Bull Ring Gang and I were making a swing in the woods behind Mrs. Thomas' house, Charlie's Nan in Maes-y-Deri, Cilfrew. Suddenly, he bounded over her back fence and was standing in front of us. I don't know if some of you know this but when he was younger, he had the loveliest curly blonde hair and it had grown so bushy that it was almost at afro status. He looked like a very pale member of the Jackson 5. "Whose gang is this?" he demanded. "Mine," I said. He looked me up and down and then uttered the phrase that I would tease him about a thousand times. "Well, I reckon I could just about handle you."

"Change the bloody record, Lynd," he said affectionately.

And handle me he did. For the next half an hour he threw me round those woods like a rag doll. I held my own at first.

I was older and faster, but he was stronger and taller. He had a two-inch height advantage on me, including his hair, about a foot. It was then that I realised that Charlie was the dirtiest fighter to ever walk God's sweet earth. He shoved soil and twigs in my mouth, leaf mould up my nose and twisted my ears like he was picking figs off a tree. We broke off for a while because Mrs. Thomas had made his tea but after that assumed the same position, him on top of me rubbing my face in the mud and carried on.

After twenty minutes, he surprisingly called it a draw which was very generous of him, bearing in mind we had to stop twice for me to be sick. From that day on we were the best of friends, and we never had a crossed word. Charlie was the only man I ever kissed on the lips, and we did this whenever we had not seen each other in a while, which in the last couple of years was far too often.

Our families were a little different to the average set up and for a few years his Dad was mine and my Mam was his."

"Good times," he reminisced.

"Charlie taught me so much about life. He taught me never to take my eyes off my sausage and chips. If I did, it was just chips. But he taught me so much more than that. He taught me never to tolerate bullies of any kind, whatever the cost, whether financial or taking a good beating. Charlie taught me to be brave, to be fearless in the face of adversity.

To take a chance, to live for the day, to punch upwards but never down, to be kind to those that need it and to bring people down a peg or two if they thought differently. Charlie taught me how to be bad, but in a really good way.

As kids, we formed the "Cilfrew Liberation Front," whose sole mission was to liberate scrap metals from their rightful owners.

This also included red diesel and on one occasion a six-foot plastic chef. We were an effective team. With his planning and my smart mouth, we were the perfect storm. I persuaded Mr. Whippy to leave his cab and check on his flat tyre whilst Charlie curled us a couple of 99s.

I climbed over the pub's back gates and passed over the pop bottles to Charlie who took them round to the bar to collect the money back on them.

Life was good.

I hope you got to see Charlie in his prime. Tall, handsome, strong. His best jeans on, new boots, immaculately ironed shirt, but not by him I hasten to add, sometimes by me, often by one of you. He had hands like digger buckets, shoulders like clifftops and a chest as wide as an estuary. When he walked into a pub everybody looked up and smiled. He brightened the moment, made your day or for some, changed their lives. If you had wronged him then him walking into a pub was like the end of days, a darkness would fall. If he ever uttered the immortal phrase, "Now listen here, my handsome boy," you knew someone was going to get their tickets punched. And a few body parts too. Most deserved it. Some did not.

"They fucking all did," reprimanded Charlie.

"I have never seen confidence or charm in such abundance in one person before or since. Going out with Charlie was like going out with a rock star, everyone knew him, loved him. It was akin to strapping yourself to a bucking bronco and hoping for the best.

Anything could happen on a night out. You could end up in the finest hotel in the South of France or a skip in Briton Ferry. I remember the time we went "prospecting" in Crynant, only to be confronted by two older boys, who were the "worse for drink," for daring to plan a hunting trip behind enemy lines.

Things got a little physical with a bit of handbags back and forth. Charlie then pointed to a fictitious spaceship on the horizon and when they searched the night sky Charlie belted one of them in the chops and took off down the middle of the road. I had no option but to wallop the other one too, before he realised what was going on.

As I caught up with Charlie with the other two in angry pursuit, I said, "Charlie, do you think we can outrun them?" He turned, not breaking a sweat, and said, "I don't need to outrun them." I said, "What the hell do you mean?" out of breath. He laughed, and shouted "I just need to outrun you," accelerating up the middle of the street. When we were together it was like he brought his own script writer with him. Things happened in his presence that could never happen to anyone else outside of the silver screen. Like the day we were walking back from Tonna Reservoir. We were about a mile in when Charlie, in a phrase catered for today's surroundings, required a bowel movement. When Charlie had to go, he had to go. I was charged with keeping a lookout. He was nearly complete when a little dog appeared and seemed extremely interested in the little gift that Charlie had left for him. Charlie, having made use of a convenient dock leaf, readjusted his apparel. I had not done a particularly good job as the last line of defence due to the hilarity of the situation. This was highlighted even further when a rather posh lady appeared at my side.

Both Charlie and I stood agog as the woman, rather apologetically announced. "My goodness Bonzo, not another one. I am so sorry, boys."

She then stooped and scooped Charlie's poop. "Good boy, Bonzo," said Charlie.

"Thank you, boys," she waved as she left with a noticeably full little bag, tied and swinging in her hand. "It was my pleasure," bowed Charlie."

"Liar, it was you that did the shit. Tell them about the time you shagged Will Jones's wife, when he was down the allotments, and you could see him out of the bedroom window." He chastised, opening another celestial brew. I faltered momentarily, looked at Widow Jones in the third row, now in her late seventies, she smiled encouragingly.

She had put her lipstick on with the back of a teaspoon. The tag from her wig hung down the middle of her forehead. I continued.

"I could keep you all day with stories of Charlie, you could too. I am sure they will all come out in the wake afterwards. I will tell you one more. We were in the field below the Red Chapel in Cilfrew. We were rolling tyres down the field trying to get them to jump the fence at the bottom and onto the football pitch and beyond. We had run out of tyres and Charlie said, "Let's roll down together, you lay on top of me, come on." "You'll bloody squash me," I said. "I know," he said, "It will be a laugh." So, we did, and it was. We laughed and laughed and cried and screamed with laughter till we could laugh no more. Up and down the field we went for what seemed like a lifetime. That one moment in time personified our very childhood. It was a moment we both looked back on as a time when only our own company mattered. Before the reality of adulthood kicked in. We never really left that moment. In our mid-twenties, walking back from Neath we did it again on the banking of Llangatwg School field. We still laughed and remembered the old times. We agreed we would do it once every ten years for the rest of our lives and we did. In our mid-thirties and the last time in our mid-forties. We drove up the Gnoll as dusk was falling, on the way out for a couple of quiet drinks.

Just two middle aged men looking for a grassy hill to climb on top of each other and to scream uncontrollably like two giddy schoolgirls. Try explaining that to the police!

We had talked about doing it again when his hernia was better. What I would not give for one more roll down that hill."

"Me too boy, me too. Come on, big finish." I heard his gravel, felt his arm around my shoulder.

I knew his game and he got me. I broke. I paused, shuffled some papers needlessly, dabbed my eyes and looked around the room. I saw the love. I felt the hate.

I saw his smile, it warmed me, as it had always done. It lifted me. I had always sought his approval. "Good boy," he said, picking me up, brushing the leaves off my face.

He pushed me back in.

"The last time I saw Charlie was a couple of months ago, I suppose before he went back into hospital. I took him to Neath to do what he called a posh shop at Marks and Spencer. He was a little slower on his feet and his words were more considered but the old Charlie was there.

We did as we always did, chatting about the old times and laughing at our adventures. Inside the supermarket, Charlie became hell bent on finding the Moroccan Chicken his sister had bought him the week before but at first it defeated us. I went one way; he went the other. Eventually we met back up and he had found it. "I'm feeling tired Lynd, can you hold this bag for me?" He was looking tired, so I did.

He put the Moroccan Chicken in his basket with his other groceries and ambled over to pay for them, which he did, but not before promising the lady at the till that when he was feeling better, he would be back to give her, in his words, "a good seeing to," a fact that she seemed rather pleased about. As we left the shop at the back entrance, heading to where Woolworths used to be, I said. "I'm glad you found the Moroccan Chicken, Charlie, you must really love it."

"I do," he said, "that's why I got three of them." I thought he might have got confused, that maybe he was not ok after all. "Charlie?" I questioned, "You only bought one, I saw you pay for it." He turned to me and smiled his big Charlie smile. "There's two more in that bag you've got, under your arm, you just fucking stole them for me."

We laughed like drains all the way home. As a last memory of him, it was a cracker."

I turned to Charlie's coffin. It was huge and beautifully vulgar, just like him.

"Charlie Boy, I am going to take the liberty of speaking on behalf of everyone here today. We loved you more than you could have known. We will miss you more than you could have ever imagined. We will speak of you often.

Sleep well, my handsome boy." xx

"You fucking show off," laughed Charlie, opening another can of heaven.

God was sitting at his side, rolling him a cigarette.

Glossary

This exhaustive Glossary was undertaken after my daughter, Joely and daughter in law (to be), Becki, read the first draft of this book. Although they claim to have enjoyed it, they were left confused by some of the points of reference and genre specific moments in the book. It made me realise, as a first-time writer of short stories, why the hell would they? Why would they understand the comparisons and analogies I made about a person, TV show or movie that they have never seen, that was made decades before they were born or books, songs and products that are not relevant to them today. This gave me two options. One, edit the obvious witty and hilarious situations out of the book, reducing the impact on every reader of my generation or two, produce this Glossary.

I decided this would also give me an opportunity to celebrate those very people, TV shows, movies, books and songs that formed me, my outlook on life and how I view the world today.

I hope it manages to open the demographic of its readership to include the young, the financially advantaged, those that are not blessed with the blood of dragons and even Americans. I also hope it will add gloss to the stories and enhance the experience.

Most of the information was gathered with the co-operation of my friends at Wikipedia.

The comments in bold italics are my own and not to be trusted in any historical context.

I would also like to use this Glossary to make a small confession to my Wife.

So convinced am I that she will never make the effort to read this book that I feel confident enough to make the following statement.

"Darling, occasionally, when I get up for a wee at night, which happens with increased frequency, I am conscious that the light in the ensuite sometimes wakes you up. As you know, I never turn the light on, and you have expressed your gratitude for my chivalry. I am sorry to say that, on the odd occasion, I have piddled in the sink so as not to take the risk of missing the toilet pan in the necessary darkness. I am not proud of this, and I promise that I will always rinse it out afterwards, run an appropriate amount of warm water and disinfect in the morning. I hope you can forgive me and my inferior genitalia for our indiscretion, but you must admit it is at a very convenient height." X

Until I receive my just desserts for this heinous crime, I will know she has not read this book. For you to tell her would simply not be Cricket.

By the way, "I don't like Cricket, oh no..."

I don't like Cricket, oh no... - "Dreadlock Holiday" is a reggae song by 10cc. Written by Eric Stewart and Graham Gouldman, it was the lead single from the band's 1978 album, Bloody Tourists. *I love it, ah, yeah.*

Introduction

Kermit the Frog - Kermit the Frog is a Muppet character created and originally performed by Jim Henson. Introduced in 1955, Kermit is the pragmatic everyman protagonist of numerous Muppet productions, most notably The Muppet Show. *The ultimate Show Frog.*

Maggie Smith - Dame Margaret Natalie Smith CH DBE is an English actress. With an extensive career on screen and stage over seven decades, she has achieved the Triple Crown of Acting, having received highest achievement for film, television and theatre, winning two Academy Awards, a Tony Award, and four Primetime Emmy Awards. *I think she is wonderful.*

Stephen Fry - Stephen John Fry is an English actor, broadcaster, comedian, director and writer. He first came to prominence in the 1980s as one half of the comic double act Fry and Laurie, alongside Hugh Laurie, with the two starring in A Bit of Fry & Laurie and Jeeves and Wooster. *Call me for a pint, Steve.*

Professor Brian Cox - Brian Edward Cox CBE FRS is an English physicist and former musician who is a professor of particle physics in the School of Physics and Astronomy at the University of Manchester and The Royal Society Professor for Public Engagement in Science. *Clever and cool.*

Mary Shelley - Mary Wollstonecraft Shelley (30 August 1797 – 1 February 1851) was an English novelist who wrote the Gothic novel Frankenstein; or, The Modern Prometheus (1818), which is considered an early example of science fiction and one of her best-known works. She also edited and promoted the works of her husband, the Romantic poet and philosopher Percy Bysshe Shelley. *Percy sounds a bit of a ponce. Mary showed him though, she has the legacy he craved.*

Victor Frankenstein - Victor Frankenstein is a fictional character and the main protagonist and title character in Mary Shelley's 1818 novel. He is a Swiss scientist, who, after studying chemical processes and the decay of living things, gains an insight into the creation of life and gives life to his own creature (often referred to as Frankenstein's monster, or often colloquially referred to as simply "Frankenstein"). *I use this as a yardstick to gauge people's intelligence, like those that say "Pacific "when they mean "Specific". Silly devils.*

Little House on the Prairie - Little House on the Prairie is an American Western historical drama television series about the Ingalls family, who live on a farm on Plum Creek near Walnut Grove, Minnesota, in the 1870s–90s. *Charles*, Laura, Caroline, Mary, and Carrie Ingalls are respectively portrayed by ***Michael Landon***, Melissa Gilbert, Karen Grassle, Melissa Sue Anderson, and twins Lindsay and Sydney Greenbush. The show is an adaptation of Laura Ingalls Wilder's best-selling series of Little House books. *I cried every episode.*

Bonanza - Bonanza is an American Western television series that ran on NBC from September 12, 1959, to January 16, 1973, and one of the longest-running, live-action American series. The show continues to air in syndication. The show is set in the 1860s and centres on the wealthy Cartwright family. *It starred Lorne Greene as Ben Cartwright.*

The Waltons - The Waltons is an American historical drama television series about a family in rural Virginia during the Great Depression and World War II. It was based on his 1961 book Spencer's Mountain and the 1963 film of the same name. The series aired from 1972 to 1981. *It starred Ralph Waite as John Walton Sr.*

Happy Days - Happy Days is an American television sitcom that aired first-run on the ABC network from January 15, 1974, to July 19, 1984, with a total of 255 half-hour episodes spanning 11 seasons. Created by Garry Marshall, it was one of the most successful series of the 1970s. The series presented an idealized vision of life in the 1950s and early 1960s Midwestern United States. *It starred Tom Bosley as Howard Cunningham.*

The Cosby Show - The Cosby Show is an American television sitcom co-created by and starring **Bill Cosby.** The series aired from September 20, 1984, to April 30, 1992, on NBC. It focuses on an upper middle-class African-American family living in Brooklyn, New York; the series was based on comedy routines in Cosby's stand-up comedy act, which in turn were based on his family life. *Unfortunately, Bill turned out to be a bit of a wrong 'un.*

The Munsters - The Munsters is an American sitcom depicting the home life of a family of benign monsters. The series stars **Fred Gwynne as Herman Munster** who looks uncannily like Frankenstein's monster. *He did not, however, look anything like Victor Frankenstein, who created the monster. Oh, for goodness' sake.*

Dylan Thomas - Dylan Marlais Thomas was a Welsh poet and writer whose works include the poems "Do not go gentle into that good night" and "And death shall have no dominion", as well as the "play for voices" Under Milk Wood. *A no good boyo whose poems meander in my soul.*

Ted Hughes - Edward James Hughes OM OBE FRSL was an English poet, translator, and children's writer. Critics frequently rank him as one of the best poets of his generation and one of the twentieth century's greatest writers. He was appointed Poet Laureate in 1984 and held the office until his death. *He taught me that poetry was not always poncey.*

Philip Larkin - Brunette Coleman was a pseudonym used by the poet and writer Philip Larkin. In 1943, towards the end of his time as an undergraduate at St John's College, Oxford, he wrote several works of fiction, verse and critical commentary under that name, including homoerotic stories that parody the style of popular writers of contemporary girls' school fiction. *Be of with Ya Larkin.*

Max Boyce - Maxwell Boyce, MBE is a Welsh comedian, singer and entertainer. He rose to fame in the mid-1970s with an act that combined musical comedy with his passion for rugby union and his origins in a South Wales mining community. *God Himself.*

Benny Hill - Alfred Hawthorne "Benny" Hill was an English comedian, actor, singer and writer. He is remembered for his television programme The Benny Hill Show, an amalgam of slapstick, burlesque and double entendre. *We lambasted Benny Hill and now we have Diet Coke adverts, Magic Mike, Babestation and Pornhub. Was he so very terrible? "Ernie the Fastest Milkman in the West," cheers me at my lowest ebb.*

Mike Harding - Mike Harding is an English singer, songwriter, comedian, author, poet, broadcaster and multi-instrumentalist. Harding has also been a photographer, traveller, filmmaker and playwright. *Just a very clever, funny man.*

Pam Ayres - Pamela Ayres MBE is a British poet, comedian, songwriter and presenter of radio and television programmes. Her 1975 appearance on the television talent show Opportunity Knocks led to appearances on other TV and radio shows, a one-woman touring stage show and performing before The Queen. *For whimsical verse she has no peers.*

Jasper Carrot - Robert Norman Davis OBE, best known by his stage name, Jasper Carrott, is an English comedian, actor, and television presenter. *My Sister and I would laugh uncontrollably to his routines. That was before she lost the ability to laugh. Read this book and please call me. X*

Bernard Cribbins - Bernard Joseph Cribbins OBE was an English actor and singer whose career spanned more than seven decades. *Before I met my actual Grandad, Bernard was my first choice.*

Ryan Davies – Ryan Davies' first professional appearance was in the National Eisteddfod of Wales in Aberavon in 1966. His talents were quickly recognised by BBC Wales, and he made his name on Welsh-language television shows. *When I heard "Napoleon vs Mam" life changed.*

Victoria Wood - Victoria Wood CBE was an English comedian, actress, lyricist, singer, composer, pianist, screenwriter, producer and director. *Probably the best comedy song writer to have ever lived yet she was so much more.*

Billy Connolly - Sir William Connolly CBE is a Scottish actor, retired comedian, artist, writer, musician, and television presenter. He is sometimes known by the Scots nickname the Big Yin. *Always top of his game. First time I'd heard "bum" and "willy" on TV.*

Ronnie Barker - Ronald William George Barker OBE was an English actor, comedian and writer. He was known for roles in British comedy television series such as Porridge, The Two Ronnies, and Open All Hours. Barker began acting in Oxford amateur dramatics whilst working as a bank clerk, having dropped out of higher education. *The master of mispronunciation. One of the great comedy writers.*

Enid Blyton - Enid Mary Blyton was an English children's writer, whose books have been worldwide bestsellers since the 1930s, selling more than 600 million copies. Her books are still enormously popular and have been translated into ninety languages. As of June 2019, Blyton held 4th place for the most translated author. *The first stories ever read to me.*

H.G. Wells - Herbert George Wells was an English writer. Prolific in many genres, he wrote more than fifty novels and dozens of short stories. His non-fiction output included works of social commentary, politics, history, popular science, satire, biography, and autobiography. *I am still haunted by "The Morlocks."*

Alexandre Dumas - Alexandre Dumas, also known as Alexandre Dumas Père, was a French novelist and playwright. His works have been translated into many languages and he is one of the most widely read French authors. *I once read his name out in class as Alexander Dumb Ass. It was a low point.*

Ian Fleming - Ian Lancaster Fleming was a British writer, best known for his post-war James Bond series of spy novels. Fleming came from a wealthy family connected to the merchant bank Robert Fleming & Co., and his father was the Member of Parliament for Henley from 1910 until his death on the Western Front in 1917. *His first choice to play Bond was Richard Burton. Can you imagine?*

Medals of Mediocrity

Betamax - Betamax is a consumer-level analogue recording and cassette format of magnetic tape for video, commonly known as a video cassette recorder. It was developed by Sony in 1975, followed by the US in November of the same year. Betamax is widely considered to be obsolete, having lost the videotape format war which saw its closest rival, VHS, dominate most markets. *I backed the wrong horse.*

Cwtch - *Cwtch* or *cwtsh* is a Welsh-language and Welsh-English dialect word meaning a cuddle or embrace, with a sense of offering warmth and safety. Often considered untranslatable, the word originated as a colloquialism in South Wales, but is today seen as uniquely representative of Wales, Welsh national identity and of Welsh culture. *But you knew that, right?*

Popeye - Popeye the Sailor Man is a fictional cartoon character. The character first appeared on January 17, 1929. *"I'm Popeye the sailor man, I live in a caravan. There's a hole in the middle, for Popeye to piddle. I'm Popeye the sailor man." Sung by my Mam's Mam, circa 1972.*

The Generation Game - The Generation Game is a British game show produced by the BBC in which four teams of two people from the same family, but different generations, compete to win prizes. *"Good game, good game."*

Green Flash - Dunlop went on to develop the iconic Dunlop Green Flash trainer which was worn and endorsed by Fred Perry when winning Wimbledon in 1934-36. The beginning of the 20th century also saw a considerable number of other companies producing shoes which utilised rubber. *Like wearing flippers when playing football.*

Kay's Catalogue - Kay & Co Ltd was a mail-order catalogue business, with offices and warehouses throughout the United Kingdom. It was a very successful company, especially during the latter part of the 20th century. *Without Kay's I would have had no new clothes at all.*

Happy Families - Happy Families is a traditional British card game usually with a specially made set of picture cards, featuring illustrations of fictional families of four, most often based on occupation types. The object of the game is to collect complete families. *Also, "Old Maid."*

Snap - Snap is a card game in which players deal cards and react quickly to spot pairs of cards of the same rank. Cards are either dealt into separate piles around the table, one per player, or (particularly when played with young children) into a single shared pile. *A card game for the aggressively daft.*

John Wayne - Marion Robert Morrison (May 26, 1907 – June 11, 1979), professionally known as John Wayne and nicknamed The Duke or Duke Wayne, was an American actor who became a popular icon through his starring roles in films which were produced during Hollywood's Golden Age, especially through his starring roles in Western and war movies. *"Get off your horse and drink your milk." I'm not sure if he ever said this but it was the basis on every impression of him.*

The Lone Ranger - The Lone Ranger is a fictional masked former Texas Ranger who fought outlaws in the American Old West with his Native American friend Tonto. The character has been called an enduring icon of American culture. *He stole William Tell's theme tune.*

Comanches - The Comanche (Comanche: "the people) are a Native American tribe from the Southern Plains of the present-day United States. Comanche people today belong to the federally recognized Comanche Nation in Oklahoma. *When Indians used to be red.*

The Nit Nurse – The Nit Nurse. A nurse who periodically checked schoolchildren's hair for lice. *Part of the Unholy Trinity. Margret Thatcher, The Grim Reaper and The Nit Nurse.*

Ali v's Foreman - George Foreman vs. Muhammad Ali, billed as *The Rumble in the Jungle*, was a heavyweight championship boxing match on October 30, 1974, at the 20th of May Stadium (now the Stade Tata Raphaël) in Kinshasa, Zaire (now Democratic Republic of the Congo). *We bought our Mam a George Foreman Grill. For years she called it her George Formby Grill.*

Cyclops - In Greek mythology and later Roman mythology, the Cyclopes, "Circle-eyes" or "Round-eyes"; singular Cyclops are giant one-eyed creatures. Three groups of Cyclopes can be distinguished. *I would like to point out that Mr Sykes had both eyes intact. Sykes/Cyclops get it?*

Jackanory - *Jackanory* is a BBC children's television series which was originally broadcast between 1965 and 1996. It was designed to stimulate an interest in reading. *Storytime for kids with no dad.*

Playmobil - Playmobil is a German line of toys produced by the Brandstätter Group. The signature Playmobil toy is a 7.5 cm tall (1:24 scale) human figure with a smiling face. A wide range of accessories, buildings and vehicles, as well as many sorts of animals, are also part of the Playmobil line. *Am I the only one that thinks these were rubbish?*

Walnut Whip - A Walnut Whip is a whirl-shaped cone of milk chocolate with a whipped vanilla fondant filling, topped with a half walnut. *The chocolate of choice for ladies of a certain age.*

Noel Edmunds - Noel Ernest Edmonds (born 22 December 1948) is an English television presenter, radio DJ, writer, producer, and businessman. Edmonds first became known as a disc jockey on Radio Luxembourg before moving to BBC Radio 1 in the UK, presenting the breakfast show for almost 5 years. He has presented various radio shows and light-entertainment television programmes for 50 years. *I have it on very good authority that he has a very Crinkly Bottom.*

Hammer House of Haircuts – Taken from the *Hammer House of Horror* which was a British horror anthology television series made in 1980. Created by Hammer Films in association with Cinema Arts International and ITC Entertainment, it consists of 13 hour-long episodes, originally broadcast on ITV. *I have a clear memory of a middle-aged Diana Dors in a baby doll nightdress. Horrifying.*

252

St John's Ambulance - St John Ambulance is the name of a number of affiliated organisations in different countries which teach and provide first aid and emergency medical services, and are primarily staffed by volunteers. The associations are overseen by the International Order of St John. *In our day, this was volunteered medical assistance dished out by people who should not be allowed to use forks or be left alone with kittens.*

Bay City Rollers - The Bay City Rollers were a Scottish pop rock band known for their worldwide teen idol popularity in the 1970s. They have been called the "tartan teen sensations from Edinburgh" and one of many acts heralded as the "biggest group since the Beatles" *Probably the worst band ever. Basically, they were muggers with microphones.*

Charlie's Angels - Charlie's Angels was an American crime drama television series that aired on ABC from September 22, 1976. It follows the crime-fighting adventures of three women working at a private detective agency in Los Angeles, California, and originally starred Kate Jackson, Farrah Fawcett (billed as Farrah Fawcett-Majors), and Jaclyn Smith in the leading roles and John Forsythe providing the voice of their boss, the unseen Charlie Townsend, who directed the crime-fighting operations of the "Angels" over a speakerphone.

It took me years to realise that Charlie was just a dirty, rich, lucky, old bastard.

Blankety Blank - Blankety Blank is a British comedy game show which started in 1979 and is still running today, albeit with some sizeable gaps. The original series ran from 18 January 1979 to 12 March 1990 on BBC1, hosted first by Terry Wogan from 1979 until 1983, then by Les Dawson from 1984 until 1990. *The set had a budget of £18.50, and they still had change.*

Terry Wogan - Sir Michael Terence Wogan KBE DL (3 August 1938 – 31 January 2016) was an Irish-British radio and television broadcaster who worked for the BBC in the UK for most of his career. His BBC Radio 2 weekday breakfast programme *Wake Up to Wogan* regularly drew an estimated eight million listeners. **The whole country still misses "Our Tel."**

Trumpton - Trumpton is a British stop-motion children's television series. First shown on the BBC from January to March 1967. The Trumptonshire trilogy, which comprised Camberwick Green, Trumpton and Chigley. **Pugh, Pugh, Barney Mcgrew, Cuthbert, Dibble, Grubb.**

Sunblest - Associated British Foods, a global PLC, still run by the Weston family. Today they bake some of the nation's favourite bakery products: top ten grocery brand Kingsmill, as well as Allinson's and Sunblest. **The empty bags were regarded as "Welsh Tupperware."**

Murderball - Murderball's origins are largely unknown. Basically, no holds barred Rugby. **Kids nearly died.**

Starsky and Hutch - Starsky & Hutch is an American action television series, which consisted of a 72-minute pilot movie and 92 episodes of 50 minutes each. The show was produced by Spelling-Goldberg Productions and starred Paul Michael Glaser and David Soul in the title roles, Starsky and Hutch. **My Mam's Mam made me a hand knitted Starsky jacket. I was so proud of it and wore it to Neath Fair. It rained on the way home and by the time I arrived my jacket weighed 2 ½ stones and came to my knees.**

Bodie and Doyle - The Professionals is a British crime-action television drama series produced by Avengers Mark1 Productions for London Weekend Television from 1977 to 1983. It starred Martin Shaw as Doyle, Lewis Collins as Bodie with Gordon Jackson as Cowley, agents of the fictional "CI5". **I so wanted to be Lewis Collins, still do.**

Bakelite - Bakelite, is a thermosetting phenol formaldehyde resin. The first plastic made from synthetic components, it was developed by Leo Baekeland in, New York in 1907, and patented on December 7, 1909. Because of its electrical nonconductivity and heat-resistant properties, it became a great commercial success. The "retro" appeal of old Bakelite products has made them collectible. *Plastic on Antiques Roadshow? This was the start of Armageddon.*

Le Mans - The 24 Hours of Le Mans is an endurance-focused sports car race held annually near the town of Le Mans, France. It is widely considered to be one of the world's most prestigious races. Run since 1923, it is the oldest active endurance racing event in the world. *It's just cars.*

Five Nations Championship - The 1990 Five Nations Championship was the 61st series of the Five Nations Championship, an annual rugby union competition between the major rugby union national teams in Europe. The tournament consisted of ten matches held between 20 January and 24 March 1990. The tournament was the 61st in its then format as the Five Nations. *Mmm, rugby.*

Urdd Eisteddfod - The Urdd National Eisteddfod (Welsh: Eisteddfod Genedlaethol Urdd Gobaith Cymru or Eisteddfod Genedlaethol yr Urdd) is an annual Welsh-language youth festival of literature, music and performing arts organised by Urdd Gobaith Cymru. It is the youth counterpart to the National Eisteddfod of Wales. *Mmm, singing.*

Woodbines - Woodbine was launched in 1888 by W.D. & H.O. Wills. Noted for its strong unfiltered cigarettes, the brand was cheap and popular in the early 20th century with the working-class, as well as with army men during the First and Second World War. *Death Fags.*

On The Buses - On the Buses is a British television sitcom that was broadcast on ITV from 1969 to 1973. It was created by Ronald Chesney and Ronald Wolfe, who wrote most of the episodes. It spawned three spin-off feature films. The series is centred on the working-class life of Stan Butler and Jack Harper, who are the crew of the Number 11 bus at the Luxton and District Motor Traction Company. The action mostly takes place at the Butler home and at the bus depot. *"I hate you, Butler." Olive was my favourite character, played by Anna Karen. She reminded me of Mam.*

Spam - Spam is a brand salty processed canned pork made by Hormel Foods Corporation. It was introduced by Hormel in 1937 and gained popularity worldwide after its use during World War II. *The breakfast of Champions. James Hunt preferred sex. It said so on his tee-shirt.*

Evel Knievel - Robert Craig Knievel (October 17, 1938 – November 30, 2007), known professionally as Evel Knievel. He was an American stunt performer and entertainer. Throughout his career, he attempted more than 75 ramp-to-ramp motorcycle jumps. He was inducted into the Motorcycle Hall of Fame in 1999. He died of pulmonary disease in Clearwater, Florida, in 2007, aged 69. *I have injured several small children, on my bike, emulating his achievements. This was not recently.*

Play For Today - Play for Today is a British television anthology drama series, produced by the BBC and transmitted on BBC1 from 1970 to 1984. During the run, more than three hundred programmes, featuring original television plays, and adaptations of stage plays and novels, were transmitted. *Quality drama, telling real stories for real people.*

Hitler – Really, you don't know who he was? *He was not a very nice man.*

Viscounts - Viscount biscuits are a classic British biscuit which consist of a circular base of biscuit, topped with a creamy mint or orange flavouring and covered with a layer of milk chocolate. They are made by Burton's Foods. *I was knocked sideways on the day I found out they were not pronounced Viss-counts. I always questioned a family's sanity if I was given an orange one.*

Corona - Corona was a brand of carbonated soft drink produced by Thomas & Evans Ltd in South Wales, and distributed across the United Kingdom. The firm was created by grocers William Thomas and William Evans when they saw a market for soft drinks caused by the growing influence of the temperance movement. *My Mam had a fictious boyfriend called "Fred the Pop."*

Penguins - Penguins are milk chocolate bars filled with biscuit and chocolate cream. They are produced by Pladis's manufacturing division McVitie's at their Stockport factory. *Overrated.*

Richard Burton - Richard Burton CBE, born Richard Walter Jenkins Jr (10 November 1925 – 5 August 1984) was a Welsh actor. Noted for his mellifluous baritone voice, Burton established himself as a formidable Shakespearean actor in the 1950s, and gave a memorable performance as Hamlet in 1964. He was called "the natural successor to Olivier" by critic Kenneth Tynan.

Burton's perceived failure to live up to those expectations disappointed some critics and colleagues; his heavy drinking added to his image as a great performer who had wasted his talent. Nevertheless, he is widely regarded as one of the finest actors of his generation. *Though never proved, it was a family rumour that my Great Grandfather, Daniel Jenkins, walked from his village in Pontrhydyfen, to my village of Cilfrew, to find work and met and married my Great Grandmother and that he was the brother of Dic Jenkins, Burton's Father. Can you imagine?*

Anita Harris - Anita Madeleine Harris (born 3 June 1942) is an English actress, singer and entertainer. Harris sang with the Cliff Adams Singers for three years from 1961 and had a number of chart hits during the 1960s. She appeared in the Carry On films Follow That Camel (1967) and Carry On Doctor (1967). *I saw her in Pantomime with Stan Stennet in the Gwyn Hall, Neath when I was a young boy and have loved her ever since. It was a sexual awakening of sorts as I had an overwhelming desire to touch her legs.*

Uncle Selwyn

Elvis - Elvis Aaron Presley (January 8, 1935 – August 16, 1977), often referred to as Elvis, was an American singer and actor. Known as the "King of Rock and Roll", he is regarded as one of the most significant cultural figures of the 20th century. *It's a little-known fact that Elvis was Welsh.*

Graceland - Graceland is a mansion on a 13.8-acre (5.6-hectare) estate in Memphis, Tennessee, United States, once owned by American singer Elvis Presley. Presley is buried there, as are his parents, paternal grandmother, grandson, and daughter. *It was rumoured he also had a caravan in Pendine Sands.*

Brian the Snail -The Magic Roundabout is an English-language children's television programme that ran from 1965 to 1977. It used the footage of the French stop motion animation show Le Manège enchanté but with completely different scripts and characters. *Yep, he was a snail.*

Yosemite Spam – Taken from Yosemite Sam is a cartoon character in the Looney Tunes and Merrie Melodies series of short films He is commonly depicted as a gunslinging outlaw or cowboy. *Yosemite Sam was a favourite mascot of a very good pal of mine, Ian Jones, who made me promise to say "nipples" in his Eulogy. He also made me promise not to tell anyone. Till now. Sleep well my friend. x*

Splitsies - In the 70s the idea was to throw the knife into the ground to make your opponent either fall over or unbalance. You threw the knife a distance from his foot, he then had to move his foot to the position of the knife, get the knife and it was his throw. You did not want to overdo the knife throw in case you did not embed in it to the ground. If you were getting overextended, you could try to get the knife in to the ground between his feet. **When good kids carried knives. I always carried a hinged, bone handled knife.**

Trowsus y Tatws – Welsh for "Potato Trousers." **Often worn with Cheese Cloth. Optional.**

Gawd Blimey Boots – Taken from a line in the popular song "My Old Man's a Dustman" which was first recorded by the British skiffle singer Lonnie Donegan. It reached number one in the British, Irish, Australian, Canadian, and New Zealand singles charts in 1960. **In the song, they are "Gawd Blimey Trousers." (Poetic Licence) Also known as "Daisy Roots," for some confusing reason.**

Mick McManus - Mick McManus (born William George Matthews; 11 January 1920 – 22 May 2013) was an English professional wrestler. The role he played was noted as a heel European wrestler and often went by the nicknames "The Man You Love to Hate", "Rugged South London Tough Guy" and "The Dulwich Destroyer". **Don't touch his ears.**

Kendo Nagasaki - Kendo Nagasaki is a professional wrestling stage name, used as a gimmick of that of a Japanese Samurai warrior with a mysterious past and even supernatural powers of hypnosis. **My Mam's Mam hated him and longed to see his mask removed. When it was, she loved him.**

Welsh Cakes - Welsh cakes (Welsh: picau ar y maen, pice bach, cacennau cri or teisennau), also bakestones or pics, are a traditional sweet bread in Wales. They have been popular since the late 19th century with the addition of fat, sugar and dried fruit to a longer standing recipe for flat-bread baked on a griddle. *My drug of choice.*

Bara Brith - traditional Welsh cake/bread flavoured with tea, dried fruits and spices. *Welsh women were judged harshly if their Bara Brith was dry. Friendships ended over it.*

Maris Pipers - Maris Piper is the most widely grown potato variety in the United Kingdom accounting for 16% of the planted area in 2014. It has been the most widely grown variety in the UK since 1980 and is suitable for a range of uses including chips, roast potatoes and mashed potatoes. *My Uncle Terry swore they were the best for chips. Now that things like this matter to me, I realise he was right.*

Cwm – Welsh for valley. *See "Pobl y Cwm," People of the Valley.*

United Welsh Buses - United Welsh Services Limited was established in 1939 to take over the various small independent bus companies which had been acquired by the Red and White Group in Swansea. The Red and White bus interests, including United Welsh Services Limited were amalgamated into the Tilling Group in 1950. In 1971 the company was taken over by South Wales Transport Company. *The important men of my family were bus drivers. The rest were wasters.*

Benny The Ball – Top Cat - Top Cat is an American animated sitcom produced by Hanna-Barbera Productions and originally broadcast in prime time on the ABC network. It was created as a parody of The Phil Silvers Show (see **Bilko**) with Arnold Stang imitating Sgt Bilko's voice for the titular character. *"Hey T.C."*

David Bowie - David Robert Jones (8 January 1947 – 10 January 2016), known professionally as David Bowie, was an English singer-songwriter and actor. A leading figure in the music industry, he is regarded as one of the most influential musicians of the 20th century. *Starman x*

Buckaroo'd - Buckaroo! is a game of physical skill, intended for players aged four and above. Buckaroo! is made by Milton Bradley, a division of the toy company Hasbro. *I broke it in 5 minutes. I also lost the luggage and had to use other items like yogurt pots and shampoo lids.*

Sailor Bags – Long, baggy, flared, trousers that were popular in the 1970's. *Yeah, Baby.*

Switzerland – A bit like Cadoxton. *I went to Switzerland once, it was -28c and I was in a tee-shirt.*

The Neath Guardian - The Neath Guardian was a local weekly newspaper published between 1925 and 2009 covering Neath, Wales, and the surrounding area. At the time of its closure, it was published weekly, on a Wednesday, in the tabloid format by Media Wales (formerly Western Mail and Echo), part of the Trinity Mirror group. *It dropped in circulation after "Jeremiah saves Neath."*

Heavy Petting – This does not mean "No large dogs in the pool." *I am still unsure of exactly what this was all about.*

Space Raiders - Space Raiders are a British brand of corn and wheat snacks made by KP Snacks. Introduced in 1987, the alien shaped snacks are currently available in Beef, Pickled Onion, Saucy BBQ and Spicy flavours. *Basically, poison in a bag. Guaranteed to strip the coating off your teeth.*

Mr Whippy - Mr. Whippy (or Mister Whippy) is a brand of soft-mix ice cream produced by Wall's, a subsidiary of Unilever as part of the Heartbrand. *With a flake, chocolate sauce and nuts, just in case you need to know. If he plays his bell, it means he has run out of Ice-cream. True.*

Valhalla - In Norse mythology Valhalla is the anglicised name for Old Norse: Valhǫll ("hall of the slain"). It is described as a majestic hall located in Asgard and presided over by the god Odin. Those who die in combat enter Valhalla. *Did you know that Vikings invented Ginger people?*

McCloud - McCloud is an American police drama television series created by Herman Miller, that aired on NBC from September 16, 1970, to April 17, 1977. The series starred Dennis Weaver, The show was centred on Deputy Marshal Sam McCloud of the small western town of Taos, New Mexico, who was on loan to the metropolitan New York City Police Department (NYPD) as a special investigator. *Very formulaic cop drama, of which there was much to choose from. Cannon was fat, McCloud had a hat. Columbo wore a Mac and Shaft? He was black.*

Steve Austin – Colonel Steve Austin is a science fiction character. He became an iconic 1970s television science fiction action hero, portrayed by American actor Lee Majors, in American television series The Six Million Dollar Man, Steve Austin takes on special high-risk government missions using his superhuman bionic powers. He became a pop culture icon of the 1970s. *Everyone had a Bionic Man action figure. Late to the shops, at Christmas, my Mam bought me an Oscar Goldman figure. Steve Austin's boss. I knew from then; my life would never run true.*

The Streets of San Francisco - The Streets of San Francisco is a television crime drama filmed in San Francisco and produced by Quinn Martin Productions, It starred Karl Malden and Michael Douglas as two homicide inspectors in San Francisco. The show ran for five seasons on ABC between 1972 and 1977, amassing a total of 119 60-minute episodes. *Karl Malden had a huge boozer's nose which I recognised from some of the old blokes in the village.*

Tigger - is a fictional and anthropomorphic stuffed tiger. He was originally introduced in the 1928 story collection The House at Pooh Corner, the sequel to the 1926 book Winnie-the-Pooh by A. A. Milne. ***We all know an irritating little shit like Tigger.***

Parkray - Parkray has been the leading name in solid fuel stoves for more than a century, producing heating components since 1850. Originally known as 'Park Foundry', the company quickly became the leading name in solid fuel appliances. ***Burnt my bum so many times, fresh out of the bath. For years I had four stipes on my backside after trying to dry by the fire.***

Jaffa Cake – Jaffa Cakes are a cake introduced by McVitie and Price in the UK in 1927 and named after Jaffa oranges. The most common form of Jaffa cakes are circular, (54 mm) in diameter and have three layers: a Genoise sponge base, a layer of orange flavoured jam and a coating of chocolate. ***They are cakes, it says so on the box. Grow up.***

Winston Churchill - Sir Winston Leonard Spencer Churchill (30 November 1874 – 24 January 1965) was a British statesman, soldier, and writer who served as Prime Minister of the United Kingdom twice, from 1940 to 1945 during the Second World War, and again from 1951 to 1955. Apart from two years between 1922 and 1924, he was a Member of Parliament (MP) from 1900 to 1964 and represented a total of five constituencies. ***Boris Johnson's hero. Hilarious.***

Spartacus - Spartacus is a 1960 American epic historical drama film directed by Stanley Kubrick, written by Dalton Trumbo, and based on the 1951 novel of the same title by Howard Fast. It is inspired by the life story of Spartacus, the leader of a slave revolt in antiquity, and the events of the Third Servile War. It stars Kirk Douglas in the title role. ***I'm Spartacus.***

Inspector Clouseau - Inspector Jacques Clouseau, is a fictional character in Blake Edwards' farcical The Pink Panther series. He is portrayed by Peter Sellers in the original series. ***"Did you say Minkey?"***

Peter Sellers - Peter Sellers CBE (born Richard Henry Sellers; 8 September 1925 – 24 July 1980) was an English actor and comedian. He first came to prominence performing in the BBC Radio comedy series The Goon Show, featured on a number of hit comic songs and became known to a worldwide audience through his many film roles, among them Chief Inspector Clouseau in The Pink Panther series. ***A comedy genius who truly believed he was.***

Monkey - Monkey, is a Japanese television drama based on the 16th-century Chinese novel Journey to the West by Wu Cheng'en. Filmed in Northwest China and Inner Mongolia, the show was produced by Nippon TV and International Television Films and broadcast from 1978 to 1980 on Nippon TV. ***Obsession would not overstate my devotion to this show.***

Samurai - Samurai were the hereditary military nobility and officer caste of medieval and early-modern Japan from the late 12th century until their abolition in the 1870s during the Meiji era. They were the well-paid retainers of the daimyo. They had high prestige and special privileges. ***Sword swingers in nice dresses.***

Tom & Jerry - Tom and Jerry is an American animated media franchise and series of comedy short films created in 1940 by William Hanna and Joseph Barbera. Best known for its 161 theatrical short films by Metro-Goldwyn-Mayer, the series centres on the rivalry between the titular characters of a cat named Tom and a mouse named Jerry. Many shorts also feature several recurring characters. ***The best ones were always directed by Fred Quimby. I only just realised; I am a nerd.***

Llanelli vs The All Blacks - 1972 – "The Day the Pubs Ran Dry"— 31 October, when Llanelli RFC defeated the touring All Blacks of New Zealand 9-3 (10-3 in today's scoring system) before a crowd of 26,000 at Stradey Park. ***Pubs throughout the town ran dry. So did the eyes of a nation.***

Brian the Snitch and the Wardrobe

Medusan – From Medusa who was a beautiful woman who was killed and beheaded by various gods. Following the moment her head was removed, a Pegasus flew out of her body, representing the birth of beauty. ***I think I danced with her once at "Mama Mia's" in Pontardawe.***

Shirley Bassey - Dame Shirley Veronica Bassey DBE is a Welsh singer. Best known for her career longevity, powerful voice and recording the theme songs to three James Bond films, Bassey is widely regarded as one of the most popular vocalists in Britain. In 1999, she was made a Dame by Queen Elizabeth II. ***I once saw a Drag Queen called "Shirley Pasty." I have to say, she was fabulous.***

The Wicker Man - The Wicker Man is a 1973 British folk horror film directed by Robin Hardy and starring Edward Woodward, Britt Ekland, Diane Cilento, Ingrid Pitt, and Christopher Lee. The screenplay is by Anthony Shaffer, inspired by David Pinner's 1967 novel Ritual. ***If you remove the "d's" from Edward Woodward's name, you get Ewar Woowar. Popular joke circa 1982.***

Ark of the Covenant - The Ark of the Covenant, also known as the Ark of the Testimony or the Ark of God, is a legendary artifact believed to be the most sacred relic of the Israelites, which is described as a wooden chest, covered in pure gold. According to the Book of Exodus, the Ark contained the two stone tablets of the Ten Commandments. ***I think I spelt Ark wrong in the book.***

Superking - Superkings was launched in 1983.The term is often used to describe any cigarette of regular gauge but with additional length to a king-sized cigarette. *Long fags.*

Bert y Biniau – Welsh for Bert the Bins. *Bert was a refuse collecting lothario.*

Chitty-Chitty-Bang-Bang - Chitty Chitty Bang Bang is a 1968 musical-fantasy film directed by Ken Hughes, produced by Albert R. Broccoli, and with a screenplay co-written by Roald Dahl and Hughes. It is loosely based on the children's novel. The film stars Dick Van Dyke, Sally Ann Howes, Lionel Jeffries. *Was originally called The Magical Car (1964) by Ian Fleming who wrote the James Bond novels. The child catcher remains one of the most terrifying characters in film history.*

Oz - From The Wizard of Oz which is a 1939 American musical fantasy film produced by Metro-Goldwyn-Mayer. An adaptation of L. Frank Baum's 1900 children's fantasy novel of the same name. *If a love of musicals means I'm gay then strike up the band, big fella.*

John Lennon - John Winston Ono Lennon (born John Winston Lennon; 9 October 1940 – 8 December 1980) was a singer, songwriter, musician, and peace activist who achieved worldwide fame as founder, co-songwriter, co-lead vocalist and rhythm guitarist of the Beatles. *Oh no Yoko.*

Flash Gordon - Flash Gordon is a 1980 space opera superhero film directed by Mike Hodges, based on the King Features comic strip of the same name created by Alex Raymond. The film stars Sam J. Jones. *He only had fourteen hours to save the Earth. He did it. We need him back.*

Sherbert Fountain - Sherbet fountains are made by Barratt. These fizzy sherbets come in packed in a small tub with a liquorice dip. These are a true retro sweet made with only natural flavours and colours. *Basically, a bit of old shoe, dipped in caustic soda.*

Superman - Superman is a superhero who appears in comic books published by DC Comics. The character was created by writer Jerry Siegel and artist Joe Shuster. *Stronger than he looked.*

Troy Tempest-Troy Tempest is the Captain of the submarine Stingray , deployed in service to, he was always ready to risk his life to defend the Earth from the dreaded aquaphibians. *"Marina, Aqua Marina." (A small mention here for Fireball XL5)*

Captain Nemo - Captain Nemo (later identified as an Indian, Prince Dakkar) is a fictional character created by the French novelist Jules Verne (1828–1905). Nemo appears in two of Verne's science-fiction classics, Twenty Thousand Leagues Under the Seas (1870) and The Mysterious Island (1875). *My kids think a sub is a sandwich. I sometimes cry in a darkened room.*

Jacques Cousteau - Jacques-Yves Cousteau, AC (11 June 1910 – 25 June 1997) was a French naval officer, oceanographer, filmmaker and author. He co-invented the first successful Aqua-Lung. The apparatus assisted him in producing some of the first underwater documentaries. *Ho, hee, ho, hee, ho.*

Octopus's Garden - Octopus's Garden is a song by the English rock band the Beatles, written and sung by Ringo Starr (credited to his real name Richard Starkey), from their 1969 album Abbey Road. *Beautiful Beatles music for kids.*

Yellow Submarine - Yellow Submarine is a song by the English rock band the Beatles from their 1966 album Revolver. Written as a children's song by Paul McCartney and John Lennon, it was drummer Ringo Starr's vocal spot on the album. *More beautiful Beatles music for kids.*

He Could Have Been a Contender

Shank's Pony – Noun – Informal. One's own legs as a means of transportation. **Still my favourite.**

The Albert Hall – In the 1970's this was the UK's premier boxing venue. **Rich, fat men with cigars.**

Madison Square Garden - In the 1970's this was New York's premier boxing venue. **See above.**

Tardis - The Tardis ("Time And Relative Dimension In Space") is a fictional time machine from the television series *Doctor Who*. Its exterior appearance mimics a police box, an obsolete type of telephone kiosk that was once commonly seen on streets in Britain. Paradoxically, its interior is shown as being much larger than its exterior, commonly described as being "bigger on the inside". **My favourite Doctor was John Pertwee. He was also my favourite Scarecrow.**

Lonsdale - Lonsdale is a British sports equipment, textile and footwear brand focused on boxing, established in London in 1960. The company is named after Hugh Lowther, 5th Earl of Lonsdale, who in 1891 set up the first organised boxing matches with gloves, following the deaths of three boxers in bare-knuckle fights. **Boxing stuff, now worn by chavs.**

The Miner's Strike - The miners' strike of 1984–1985 was a major industrial action within the British coal industry. It was led by Arthur Scargill of the National Union of Mineworkers (NUM) Opposition to the strike was led by Prime Minister Margaret Thatcher, who wanted to reduce the power of the trade unions. **Tough times.**

Motability Scooter - A mobility scooter is an electric vehicle and mobility aid mostly auxiliary to a power wheelchair but configured like a motor scooter. When motorized they are commonly referred to as a power-operated vehicle/scooter, or electric scooter. ***I'm getting one, one day.***

Paul Newman - Paul Leonard Newman (January 26, 1925 – September 26, 2008) was an American actor, film director, race car driver, philanthropist, and entrepreneur. ***Mam loved him.***

Mackintosh - Mackintosh raincoat (abbreviated as mac) is a form of waterproof raincoat, first sold in 1824, made of rubberised fabric. ***Often worn by the penis revealing elite.***

Get the Hell out of Dodge - An allusion to Dodge City, Kansas, a busy cattle town in the late 19th century notorious for gunfighters, gambling, brothels and saloons. Possibly inspired by the radio and television series Gunsmoke (1952-1975). ***There were times when Neath was a bit Dodgy.***

The Racing Post - Racing Post is a British daily horse racing, greyhound racing and sports betting publisher which is published in print and digital formats. It is printed in tabloid format from Monday to Sunday. ***Reading for the financially disillusioned.***

Cunt – Not a nice word. ***Occasionally used to describe a person who is otherwise indescribable.***

He could have been a contender - This, famous lament is spoken by Terry Malloy, played by Marlon Brando, in On the Waterfront. Used for saying that somebody could have been successful at something but were not. ***Commonly used to describe boxers who did not reach their potential.***

Windy Hill Farm

Woodpecker - Woodpecker Cider is a sweet cider originally made in 1894 by Percy Bulmer in Herefordshire and today brewed by H. P. Bulmer. Woodpecker is noted for a lower alcohol content than most other ciders as well as for its sweet taste. *Entry level booze for kids hoping to become alcoholics someday.*

The Beano - The Beano is a British anthology comic magazine created by Scottish publishing company DC Thomson. Its first issue was published on 30 July 1938, and it published its 4000th issue in August 2019. *Without The Beano there would be no Viz. I love Viz.*

Russian Roulette - Russian roulette is a potentially lethal game of chance in which a player places a single round in a revolver, spins the cylinder, places the muzzle against the head or body (of the opponent or themselves), and pulls the trigger. *There is a certain Russian who needs to play this.*

The Deer Hunter - The Deer Hunter is a 1978 epic war drama film co-written and directed by Michael Cimino about a trio of Slavic-American steelworkers whose lives were upended after fighting in the Vietnam War. The three soldiers are played by Robert De Niro, Christopher Walken, and John Savage. *One of the greatest films ever made.*

The Charge of the Light Brigade - The Charge of the Light Brigade was a military action undertaken by British light cavalry against Russian forces during the Battle of Balaclava in the Crimean War, resulting in many casualties to the cavalry. *I wore a balaclava, itchy but warm.*

Massey Ferguson - Massey Ferguson Limited is an American agricultural machinery manufacturer. The company was established in 1953 through the merger of farm equipment makers Massey-Harris of Canada and the Ferguson Company of the United Kingdom. *Drove my first one at 11.*

Messrs. Hughes, Morgan, Manley and Morgan

Ovaltine -Ovaltine is a brand of milk flavouring product made with malt extract, sugar and whey. Some flavours also have cocoa. ***Malty hot chocolate for heroes.***

St Bruno – St Bruno Flake is a distinctive blend of smooth Virginia and smoky dark fired Kentucky pie tobacco, pressed and sliced into thin flakes that are easy to prepare. ***Memories of my Gags.***

Mungo Jerry - Mungo Jerry is a British rock band, formed by Ray Dorset in Ashford, Middlesex in 1970. Experiencing their greatest success in the early 1970s, with a changing lineup always fronted by Dorset, the group's biggest hit was "In the Summertime." ***It contained the line "Have a drink, have a drive, go and see what you can find."***

Spike Milligan - Terence Alan "Spike" Milligan KBE was a British comedian, writer, musician, poet, playwright, and actor. He was born in British Colonial India, where he spent his childhood before relocating in 1931 to England. ***Spike was in the same regiment as my Grandad Reg, along with a local lad, Harry Secombe.***

Spike wrote my favourite poem of all time. It has everything, in four lines.

"One day I thought I saw,

Jesus on a tram,

I said to him 'Are You Jesus?'

He said 'Yes I am.'"

Ronnie Corbett - Ronald Balfour Corbett CBE (4 December 1930 – 31 March 2016) was a Scottish actor, broadcaster, comedian and writer. He had a long association with *Ronnie Barker* in the BBC television comedy sketch show The Two Ronnies. He achieved prominence in David Frost's 1960s satirical comedy programme The Frost Report. *If you have not walked into an old-style Ironmongers and not asked for "Four Candles" then we cannot be friends.*

O Levels – Proper qualifications from a time before I developed original thought. *Did I mention I have 11?*

Welcome to my parlour said the spider to the fly - "The Spider and the Fly" is a poem by Mary Howitt (1799–1888), published in 1829. The first line of the poem is "'Will you walk into my parlour?' said the Spider to the Fly." The story tells of a cunning spider who entraps a fly into its web using seduction and manipulation. The poem is a cautionary tale against those who use flattery and charm to disguise their true intentions. *I was pretty smooth, back in the day.*

Windsor Davies - Windsor Davies (28 August 1930 – 17 January 2019) was a British actor. He is best remembered for playing Battery Sergeant Major Williams in the sitcom It Ain't Half Hot Mum (1974–1981) over its entire run. *"Now then, now then, my lovely boys."*

Gotham City - Gotham City, or simply Gotham, is a fictional city appearing in American comic books published by DC Comics, best known as the home of the superhero Batman/ Bruce Wayne and his allies and foes. *A bit like Merthyr Tydfil on bin day.*

Lurex - Lurex is the registered brand name of the Lurex Company, Ltd. for a type of yarn with a metallic appearance. *Chaffed like buggery.*

Moonwalking - The moonwalk or backslide is a dance move in which the performer glides backwards but their body actions suggest forward motion. It became popular around the world. Michael Jackson popularized the moonwalk during the performance of "Billie Jean." *Hee- hee, shamon. I am so confused whether to still love Michael Jackson's music.*

Marcel Marceau - Marcel Marceau, born Marcel Mangel; 22 March 1923 – 22 September 2007) was a French mime artist and actor most famous for his stage persona, "Bip the Clown". He referred to mime as the "art of silence", performing professionally worldwide for more than 60 years. *(I have left this section without comment in honour of his wonderful silent comedy)*

Felatio – A mythical state of extasy whispered about in shadowy corners when married men get together. *I may get into trouble over this bit.*

Kung Fu - Kung Fu is an American action-adventure martial arts Western drama television series starring David Carradine. The series follows the adventures of Kwai Chang Caine, a Shaolin monk who travels through the American Old West, armed only with his spiritual training and his skill in martial arts, as he seeks Danny Caine, his half-brother. *Was Hong Kong Phooey his dog?*

Porshe – Porshes are cars for generally small men with very small penises. *Usually driven by men called Rex or Tobias.*

Tom Selleck - Thomas William Selleck (born January 29, 1945) is an American actor. His breakout role was playing private investigator Thomas Magnum in the television series Magnum, P.I. (1980–1988), for which he received five Emmy Award nominations for Outstanding Lead Actor in a Drama Series, winning in 1985. *Top Tache.*

Freddie Mercury - Freddie Mercury (born Farrokh Bulsara; 5 September 1946 – 24 November 1991) was a British singer and songwriter, who achieved worldwide fame as the lead vocalist of the rock band Queen. Regarded as one of the greatest singers in the history of rock music, he was known for his flamboyant stage persona and four-octave vocal range. *I'm pretty sure he was Welsh.*

Rank Cinema – See Arthur Rank – **Mr Wood**

The Warriors - The Warriors is a 1979 American action thriller film directed by Walter Hill. Based on Sol Yurick's 1965 novel of the same name. The film centres on a fictitious New York City street gang who are framed for the murder of a respected gang leader. *The start of a genre.*

The Wanderers - The Wanderers is a 1979 American film co-written and directed by Philip Kaufman. Set in the Bronx in 1963, the film follows a gang of Italian American teenagers known as the Wanderers and their ongoing power struggles with rival gangs such as the Baldies and the Wongs. *A real classic film.*

Death Race 2000 - Death Race 2000 is a 1975 American science fiction action film produced by Roger Corman, directed by Paul Bartel, and starring David Carradine. The film takes place in a dystopian American society in the year 2000, where the murderous Transcontinental Road Race has become a form of national entertainment. The screenplay is based on the short story The Racer by Ib Melchior. *I remember that someone did a wheel spin on a fella's old fella. Gruesome.*

Space Invaders -Space Invaders is a 1978 shoot 'em up arcade video game developed by Tomohiro Nishikado. It was manufactured and sold by Taito in Japan. *Played by boys with no hope of ever having a snog.*

Panda Pop – Panda Pop were small bottles of fluorescent fizzy drinks and were a staple of school discos in the 1980's. They were cheap and cheerful soft drinks full of lots of ingredients (they were very sweet and sugary) that probably wouldn't see the light of day today. ***Turps with sugar.***

Rainbow Drops - Rainbow Drops are a brand of sugar-coated cereal-type   puffed maize and rice   confectionery sold   in both Ireland and   the United   Kingdom and   produced by Swizzels, Matlow. The sweets have an orange, pink, green and yellow coloured sugary coating. ***One packet contained enough E numbers to kill a Bison.***

Refreshers - Refreshers are one of Swizzels' most popular products. These are flat chewy sweets with sherbet in the middle, available in lemon and strawberry flavours. ***Removed stomach linings.***

Black Jacks - Back jack chews by Barratt - the original old penny aniseed flavour chew. Approximately 40 sweets per bag. Please note these are now the new square shape. Also available to buy by the whole box of 400 chews. ***Thieves were caught instantly. Black tongues.***

Trimphone - The Trimphone is a model of telephone designed in the late-1960s in the UK. The name is an acronym standing for Tone   Ring   Illuminator   Model,   referring   to   the   then innovative electronic ringer ("warbling", as opposed to the traditional bell) and the illuminated dial. ***There were national Trimphone impersonation competitions on live TV. They were such innocent times.***

DLT - David   Patrick   Griffin (born   25   May   1945), known professionally as Dave Lee Travis, is an English disc jockey, radio presenter and television presenter. ***"Quack, quack oops."***

Tony Blackburn - Anthony Kenneth Blackburn (born 29 January 1943) is an English disc jockey, singer and TV presenter. He first achieved fame broadcasting on the pirate stations, before joining the BBC. *He never got over Tessa Wyatt. (Google her, I'm losing the will to live.)*

Zoom by Fat Larry's Band - "Zoom" is a song by American band Fat Larry's Band released in 1982. *Responsible for more erections than Viagra. The most popular last dance of the evening.*

Toffos - Toffo was a British brand of toffee, produced by Mackintosh's. They came individually wrapped, in a roll, and were available in plain, mint, and assorted (apple, strawberry, pineapple, banana, and mint) flavours. *Responsibly for 93% of loose fillings (Welsh Dental Association).*

Portakabins - A portable, demountable or transportable building is a building designed and built to be movable rather than permanently located. *Usually a sign of an underfunded local authority.*

Finding Albert

Vaseline - Vaseline is an American brand of petroleum jelly-based products owned by transnational company Unilever. *It's sad to remember the imaginative ways I have used Vaseline in years gone by and now I use it to stop my pendulous testicles from chaffing and my nipples from rubbing if I go jogging.*

Insulation Tape - Electrical tape, also referred to as *insulating tape*, is used to insulate wiring that conducts electricity. *Once, it was the only tape.*

Deep Heat - Deep Heat Pain Relief Spray is a pain relieving, warming spray. It is recommended for the relief of pain in muscles. *It has the opposite effect on certain parts of your anatomy.*

Jock Straps – Recommended bindings when planning to kidnap a person of Scottish heritage. *Ha!*

Barry Butlins – Butlins holiday resort in the Welsh seaside town of Barry. *Known locally as Pont y Disney.*

Michael Bentine - Michael Bentine's Potty Time was a British children's show, written by and starring Michael Bentine for Thames Television on ITV. It ran from 1973 to 1980. The episodes consisted largely of bearded puppets (called "Potties"), comically re-enacting famous historical situations. The Potties' faces were always obscured by facial hair, with only their noses protruding. *Another Goon I loved to watch.*

Scirocco – A pretty cool car in the 1980's. *Driven by men with no hope of finding girlfriends.*

Kajagoogoo – Kajagoogoo were a gender fluid pop band from the 1980's. *They were truly awful and sadly ahead of their time.*

Readybrek - Ready Brek (stylized as Ready brek) is an oat-based breakfast cereal produced by Weetabix Limited. It is intended to be served hot and comes in two varieties — 'original' and 'chocolate'. Other variants were available but have since been discontinued. TV adverts showed a Readybrek "glow" around you to fight off cold mornings. *I found a vest was a better option and stuck with Weetabix.*

Baron's Night Club - The legendary Swansea nightclub closed down in August 2006 after 55 eventful years in various guises. *More dangerous than the Gaza Strip with worse toilet facilities.*

Borstal - A Borstal was a type of youth detention centre in the United Kingdom, several member states of the Commonwealth and the Republic of Ireland. *Basically, prison prep school.*

Milliner - Millinery is the design, manufacture and sale of hats and other headwear. A person engaged in this trade is called a milliner. **LOVE HATS, get it?**

Bobby Moore - Robert Frederick Chelsea Moore OBE (12 April 1941 – 24 February 1993) was an English professional footballer. He was captain of West Ham United and the England national team that won the 1966 FIFA World Cup. **Great also in "Escape to Victory," with Pele, Sylvester Stallone and Michael Caine.**

Bluebird – Cardiff City FC have been blue and white since 1908, from which their nickname "The Bluebirds" derives. Cardiff's first ground was Ninian Park, which opened in 1910. **Boo!**

Reactolite - The principle of a Reactolite lens is when exposed to UV light the lenses will darken grey in colour. **In the 1980's they were regarded as eyewear for the spatially unaware.**

Piss on my chips - Being a spoilsport or dampening the mood of something which would otherwise be fun. Pissing on someone else's chips is spoiling their fun/day/activity/whatever. **I've tried never to do this. I hope that I have succeeded.**

Iesu Grist - Welsh for Jesus Christ. **It's a little-known fact that Jesus was Welsh.**

Grange Hill - Grange Hill is a British children's television drama series, originally produced by the BBC and portraying life in a typical comprehensive school. The show began its run on 8 February 1978 on BBC1, and was one of the longest-running programmes on British television. It was created by Phil Redmond. **"Just say no."**

Perspex - Poly(methyl methacrylate) (PMMA) is the synthetic polymer derived from methyl methacrylate. Being an engineering plastic, it is a transparent thermoplastic. PMMA is also known as acrylic, acrylic glass. **Council Glass.**

Austin Maxi - The Austin Maxi is a medium-sized, 5-door hatchback family car that was produced by Austin and later British Leyland between 1969 and 1981. It was the first British five-door hatchback. *I'm pretty sure they were sprayed with the left-over paints at the factory.*

Jimmy Saville - Sir James Wilson Vincent Savile OBE KCSG (31 October 1926 – 29 October 2011) was an English DJ and television and radio personality who hosted BBC shows including Top of the Pops and Jim'll Fix It. *I wrote to Jim to ask if he could fix it for me to go camping with Gary Glitter and Rolf Harris but he never wrote back. Cunt.*

Charlie Bucket - Charlie and the Chocolate Factory is a 1964 children's novel by British author Roald Dahl. The story features the adventures of young Charlie Bucket inside the chocolate factory of eccentric chocolatier Willy Wonka. *I knew a Charlene Bucket once.*

Brut 33 - Brut was launched in 1964 by the American firm Fabergé Inc. and has been owned since 1990 by the British multinational company Unilever. *"Splash it all over."*

Oh, Lyndon bach, mae fy machgen adref – Oh, Lyndon, my little boy is home. *I miss you, Nan. x*

Mamgu and Tadgu – Welsh for Grandma and Grandad.

Rwy'n dy garw – I love you. *I love you too, Joce. x*

Lyndon bach, dod yma – Come here Lyndon.

Yellow Pages - The Yellow Pages are telephone directories of businesses, organized by category rather than alphabetically by business name, in which advertising is sold. *Heavy, back in the day.*

Metal Box - The former Metal Box factory is one of Neath's most iconic buildings. It was originally producer of printed metal boxes for biscuits etc. A major employer in the Neath area. *Just boxes.*

Barry John - Barry John (born 6 January 1945) is a former Welsh and British Lions rugby union fly-half who played, during the amateur era of the sport, in the 1960s, and early 1970s. John began his rugby career as a schoolboy playing for his local team Cefneithin RFC before switching to first-class West Wales team Llanelli RFC in 1964. It was while at Llanelli that John was first selected for the Wales national team, a shock selection as a replacement for David Watkins to face a touring Australian team. *God made him on his day off.*

Tafia – The Welsh Mafia. *This is not a joke.*

Waltzers - A Waltzer is a flat fairground ride that often forms the centrepiece of traditional British and Irish fairs. The ride consists of a number of cars which spin freely while rotating around a central point, in much the same way as a carousel. *Operated by thieving, oversexed deviants.*

Iron Maiden - Iron Maiden are an English heavy metal band formed in Leyton, East London, in 1975. *I never understood the music of the great unwashed, Spandau Ballet were my Rock Gods.*

Zorro - Zorro (Spanish for 'fox') is a fictional character created in 1919 by American pulp writer Johnston McCulley, appearing in works set in the Pueblo of Los Angeles in Alta California. His signature all-black costume includes a cape, a hat, and a mask covering the upper half of his face. *My Dad was Zorro. Maybe he still is? I'll get back to you on that.*

A Star-Spangled Manner

Mark Zuckerberg - Mark Elliot Zuckerberg (born May 14, 1984) is an American computer programmer, business magnate, internet entrepreneur and philanthropist. He is known for co-founding the social media website Facebook. *What have you done, Mark?*

Cameron Diaz - Cameron Michelle Diaz (born August 30, 1972) is an American actress. She has received various accolades, including nominations for four Golden Globe Awards and a British Academy Film Award. As of 2018, her films have grossed over $3 billion in the U.S. *She has never been The Prime Minister of the UK.*

The Breakfast Club - The Breakfast Club is a 1985 American independent teen coming-of-age comedy-drama film written, produced, and directed by John Hughes. The film tells the story of five teenagers from different high school cliques who serve a Saturday detention overseen by their authoritarian vice-principal. *A pretty bad film with hindsight.*

Swan Vesta - Swan Vestas is a brand of matches. Shorter than normal pocket matches, they are particularly popular with smokers and have long used the tagline "the smoker's match." *Big box.*

The Dukes of Hazzard - The Dukes of Hazzard is an American action comedy TV series that was aired on CBS from January 26, 1979 to February 8, 1985. The show aired for 147 episodes spanning seven seasons. It was consistently among the top-rated television series in the late 1970s. *Daisy Duke, oh my goodness. Her shorts were so short, you could see her breakfast.*

G.I. – G. I. was reinterpreted as "government issue" or "general issue." The prevalence of the term led soldiers in World War II to start referring to themselves as GIs. Some servicemen used it as a sarcastic reference symbolizing their belief that they were just mass-produced products of the government. *I had an Auntie (who shall remain nameless) who would do anything for a Hersey Bar and a pair of stockings.*

Panzer - The Panzer was the most numerous German tank and the second-most numerous German fully tracked armoured fighting vehicle of the Second World War. *Schnell.*

Choose Life – Choose Life tee shirts were worn by George Michael and Andrew Ridgeley of Wham! in their video for the song Wake Me Up Before You Go-Go. The slogan is promoting an anti-drug and anti-suicide campaign. Choose Life was printed on both the front and back of the shirt. *"You put the boom, boom into my heart." It was impossible not to dance to this in the 80's.*

George Michael - George Michael (born Georgios Kyriacos Panayiotou; 25 June 1963 – 25 December 2016) was an English singer-songwriter and record producer. He is one of the best-selling musicians of all time, with his sales estimated at between 100 million and 125 million records worldwide. *I didn't know. Nobody did. I miss George. One of the good guys.*

Club Tropicana - "Club Tropicana" was written in 1981 in Ridgeley's living room, before the band or band name had been fully established and was the second Wham! song they came up with after the initial "Wham Rap!" *I am led to believe the drinks were very reasonably priced.*

St Elmo's Fire - St. Elmo's Fire is a 1985 American coming-of-age film co-written and directed by Joel Schumacher. It received negative reviews from critics but was a box-office hit, grossing $37.8 million on a $10 million budget. *Another dreadful movie that seemed important at the time.*

Faggot - Faggot, often shortened to fag, is a term, usually a pejorative, used to refer to gay men. In American youth culture around the turn of the 21st century, its meaning extended as a broader reaching insult more related to masculinity and group power structure. *Cheeky devil.*

Faggot - Faggots are meatballs made from minced off-cuts and offal (especially pork, and traditionally pig's heart, liver, and fatty belly meat or bacon) mixed with herbs and sometimes bread crumbs. It is a traditional dish in the United Kingdom. *Welsh faggots rock.*

Biff, "Back to the Future," Bastard - Biff Tannen is a fictional character and a major antagonist in the Back to the Future trilogy. Thomas F. Wilson plays Biff in all three films. ***Chet was Biff.***

Whistling Dixie – To engage in unrealistic, hopeful fantasizing, as in If you think you can drive there in two hours, you're whistling Dixie. This idiom alludes to the song "Dixie" and the vain hope that the Confederacy, known as Dixie, would win the Civil War. ***"Oh, I wish I was.."***

Ronnie and Reggie - Ronald Kray (24 October 1933 – 17 March 1995) and Reginald Kray (24 October 1933 – 1 October 2000) were identical twin brothers and gangsters, who were the foremost perpetrators of organised crime in the East End of London, England, from the late 1950s to 1967. With their gang, known as the Firm, the Kray twins were involved in murder, armed robbery, arson, protection rackets, gambling, and assaults. ***Bad men with style.***

Sam Elliot - Samuel Pack Elliott (born August 9, 1944) is an American actor. He is the recipient of several accolades, including a Screen Actors Guild Award, and a National Board of Review Award, and has been nominated for an Academy Award, two Golden Globe Awards, and two Emmy Awards. Elliott is known for his distinctive lanky physique, full moustache, and a deep, sonorous voice. ***In the dictionary under "Cool."***

Danny Devito -Daniel Michael DeVito Jr. (born November 17, 1944) is an American actor, comedian, and filmmaker. He gained prominence for his portrayal of the taxi dispatcher Louie De Palma in the television series Taxi (1978–1983), which won him a Golden Globe Award and an Emmy Award. ***Played The Penguin in "Batman Returns." He should have got an Oscar.***

Patrick Swayze - Patrick Wayne Swayze (August 18, 1952 – September 14, 2009) was an American actor, dancer, and singer-songwriter known for playing distinctive lead roles, particularly romantic, tough, and comedic characters. People magazine named Swayze the "Sexiest Man Alive" in 1991. *The man could fight and dance. I am poor at both.*

World of Sport with Dickie Davies – World of Sport was produced by London Weekend Television (LWT) under the ITV Sport banner and hosted by Dickie Davies, who would remain the face of the show until it ended in 1985. *Women watched just to see Dickie. Suave and debonair.*

Delilah, Green, Green Grass of Home – Songs of Sir Thomas Jones Woodward OBE (born 7 June 1940) who is a Welsh singer. His career began with a string of top 10 hits in the 1960s and he has since toured regularly, with appearances in Las Vegas from 1967 to 2011. *I played Sir Tom's voice in an Audiobook. "Just Help Yourself." Great fun and available now on suitable platforms.*

Hen Wlad Fy Nhadau - "Hen Wlad Fy Nhadau" (Welsh pronunciation: [heːn wlaːd və n̥adai]) is the unofficial national anthem of Wales. The title, taken from the first words of the song, means "Old Land of My Fathers" in Welsh. *It's been an honour to serve.*

JPR Williams - John Peter Rhys Williams MBE FRCS (born 2 March 1949) is a former Welsh rugby union player who represented Wales in international rugby during their Golden Era in the 1970s. He became known universally as J. P. R. Williams (or sometimes just as JPR) after 1973 when J. J. Williams (also John) joined the Welsh team. *Looked all wrong but was so very right.*

Candid Camera - Candid Camera is an American hidden camera reality television series. Versions of the show appeared on television from 1948 until 2014. Originally created and produced by Allen Funt, it often featured practical jokes. **The first of its kind and the best.**

Pontypool Front Row - The Pontypool Front Row also known as the "Viet Gwent", (motto "We may go down; we may go up; but we never go back") was made up of Graham Price, Bobby Windsor and Charlie Faulkner and played as a unit 19 times for Wales, only finishing on the losing side four times. They also played as a unit for the British and Irish Lions in several midweek matches and the final test match against Fiji. **The epitome of the Welsh physique. Legends all.**

Summer of Love -The Summer of Love was a social phenomenon that occurred during the summer of 1967, when as many as 100,000 people, mostly young people sporting hippie fashions of dress and behaviour, converged in San Francisco's neighbourhood of Haight-Ashbury. More broadly, the Summer of Love encompassed the hippie music, hallucinogenic drugs, anti-war, and free-love scene throughout the West Coast of the United States, and as far away as New York City. **I bet Strongbow was not £10 pound a pint.**

Mr Wood

Frances De La Tour - Frances J. de Lautour (born 30 July 1944), better known as Frances de la Tour, is an English actress. She is known for her role as Miss Ruth Jones in the television sitcom Rising Damp from 1974 until 1978. She is a Tony Award winner and three-time Olivier Award winner. "**Ohh, Miss Jones.**"

Mother Teresa - Mary Teresa Bojaxhiu MC (26 August 1910 – 5 September 1997), better known as Mother Teresa, was an Albanian-Indian Catholic nun and the founder of the Missionaries of Charity. *Thank you.*

The Banbury Guardian - The Banbury Guardian is a local tabloid newspaper published in Banbury, Oxfordshire. It serves north Oxfordshire, southwest Northamptonshire and southeast Warwickshire. *Real local newspapers like this are dying out. A real shame.*

Walkman - Walkman, is a brand of portable audio players manufactured and marketed by Japanese technology company Sony since 1979. The original Walkman was a portable cassette player. *Never had one, never wanted one. I do, however love my Alexa. She understands me.*

Charlie Chaplin - Sir Charles Spencer Chaplin KBE (16 April 1889 – 25 December 1977) was an English comic actor, filmmaker, and composer who rose to fame in the era of silent film. He became a worldwide icon through his screen persona, the Tramp, and is considered one of the film industry's most important figures. *"The Great Dictator" was a work of pure genius.*

Will Hay - William Thomson Hay FRAS (6 December 1888 – 18 April 1949) was an English comedian who wrote and acted in a schoolmaster sketch that later transferred to the screen, where he also played other authority figures with comic failings. *A brilliant character comedian.*

Blockbusters - Blockbuster LLC, formerly known as Blockbuster Video, is an American brand (and defunct national video rental store chain). It was originally founded by David Cook in 1985 as a stand-alone home video rental shop, but later grew into a national store chain featuring video game rentals, DVD-by-mail, streaming, video on demand, and cinema theatre. *I miss going.*

Willy Wonka - Willy Wonka is a fictional character appearing in British author Roald Dahl's 1964 children's novel Charlie and the Chocolate Factory and its 1972 sequel Charlie and the Great Glass Elevator. *Gene Wilder as Willy Wonka was beyond magical, I loved his work.*

Dr Dolittle - Doctor Dolittle is a 1967 American musical comedy film directed by Richard Fleischer and starring Rex Harrison. It was adapted by Leslie Bricusse from the Doctor Dolittle novel series by Hugh Lofting. *Memories of Rex Harrison speaking/singing makes me smile.*

Arthur Rank - The Rank Organisation (founded as J. Arthur Rank), was a British entertainment conglomerate founded by industrialist J. Arthur Rank in April 1937, Rank also served as the company chairman. *Cockney rhyming slang for a five-knuckle shuffle.*

Gallé - Émile Gallé (8 May 1846 – 23 September 1904) was a French artist and designer who worked in glass, and is considered to be one of the major innovators in the French Art Nouveau movement. *Glass is very beautiful.*

Lalique - René Jules Lalique (6 April 1860 – 1 May 1945) was a French jeweller, medallist, and glass designer known for his creations of glass art, perfume bottles, vases, jewellery. Chandeliers, clocks and automobile hood ornaments. *Seriously, check out his hood ornaments, amazing.*

Yul Brynner - Yuliy Borisovich Briner (July 11, 1920 – October 10, 1985), known professionally as Yul Brynner, was a Russian-born actor. He was best known for his portrayal of King Mongkut in the Rodgers and Hammerstein stage musical The King and I. *Please watch him in the original "Westworld", wow.*

Last Night of the Proms - Many people's perception of the Proms is based on the Last Night, although this is very different from the other concerts. It usually takes place on the second Saturday in September, and is broadcast in the UK on BBC Radio 3, BBC Two and BBC One. *Music enjoyed by numpties. The music is amazing, the numpties, not so much.*

Harrods - Harrods Limited is a department store located on Brompton Road in Knightsbridge, London, England. It is currently owned by the state of Qatar and previously the Al Fayed Brothers. The Harrods brand also applies to other enterprises undertaken by the Harrods group of companies. *The haves and the have nots. Harrods makes me a little sad.*

The Mallard – The Mallard steam locomotive built in 1938 to a design of Nigel Gresley. Its streamlined, wind tunnel tested design allowed it to haul long distance express passenger services at high speeds. On 3 July 1938, Mallard broke the world speed record for steam locomotives at 126 mph (203 km/h), which still stands. *It never looked like a duck to me.*

Pullman Carriage - Pullman trains in Great Britain were mainline luxury railway services that operated with first-class coaches and a steward service, provided by the British Pullman Car Company from 1874 until 1962. *Very posh trains where murder often occurred.*

Moet & Chandon - Moët & Chandon, also known simply as Moet. Moët et Chandon is one of the world's largest champagne producers and a prominent champagne house. Moët et Chandon was established in 1743 by Claude Moët, and annually produces approximately 28,000,000 bottles of champagne. *Best kept in a pretty cabinet. My favourite opening line to a song. "Killer Queen."*

The Salvation Army - The Salvation Army is a Protestant Christian church and an international charitable organization headquartered in London, England. It is aligned with the Wesleyan-Holiness movement. *At a low point in my life, I was saved by a Captain in the Salvation Army called Pearl. Still, I keep her card in my wallet. She is an angel.*

Thomas the Tank Engine - Thomas the Tank Engine is an anthropomorphised fictional tank locomotive in the British Railway Series books by Wilbert Awdry and his son, Christopher, published from 1945. He became the most popular and famous character in the series. *I always wondered if the Fat Controller was the Rev getting one over on the reader. Like Seaman Stains and Master Bates in Captain Pugwash?*

Magnum P.I. - Magnum, P.I. is an American crime drama television series starring Tom Selleck as Thomas Magnum, a private investigator (P.I.) living on Oahu, Hawaii. The series ran from December 11, 1980, to May 8, 1988. *Top Tache with a Ferrari.*

Mr Al Fayed - Mohamed Al-Fayed (born 27 January 1929) is an Egyptian-born businessman whose residence and chief business interests have been in the United Kingdom since the late 1960s. His business interests include ownership of Hôtel Ritz Paris and formerly Harrods department store and Fulham F.C. *I met him again, years later at Fulham FC, he still seemed very nice.*

Walter Mitty - Walter Jackson Mitty is a fictional character in James Thurber's first short story "The Secret Life of Walter Mitty", first published in The New Yorker on March 18, 1939. Thurber loosely based the character, a daydreamer, on himself. It was made into a film in 1947 starring Danny Kaye. *Danny Kaye was a big hero of mine.*

Goldfinger - "Goldfinger" is the title song from the 1964 James Bond film Goldfinger. Composed by John Barry and with lyrics by Leslie Bricusse and Anthony Newley, the song was performed by Shirley Bassey for the film's opening and closing title sequences, as well as the soundtrack album release. *"He's the man, the man with the Midas touch. A spider's touch."*

Eric Morecambe - John Eric Bartholomew OBE, known by his stage name Eric Morecambe, was an English comedian who together with Ernie Wise formed the double act Morecambe and Wise. The partnership lasted from 1941 until Eric's death in 1984. *Even his socks made me laugh.*

Nutcracker Suite - The Nutcracker is an 1892 two-act "fairy ballet" by Pyotr Ilyich Tchaikovsky, set on Christmas Eve at the foot of a Christmas tree in a child's imagination. *Beautiful.*

River Danced - Riverdance is a theatrical show that consists mainly of traditional Irish music and dance. With a score composed by Bill Whelan, it originated as an interval act during the Eurovision Song Contest 1994, featuring Irish dancing champions Jean Butler and Michael Flatley. *He's got some ego, that Flatley fella. (Read this in an Irish accent, for full effect)*

The Eulogy of Keith Charles Thomas

Owain Glyndwr - Owain ap Gruffydd (c. 1354 – c. 1415), commonly known as Owain Glyndŵr or Glyn Dŵr, anglicised as Owen Glendower, was a Welsh leader, soldier and military commander who led a 15-year-long revolt with the aim of ending English rule in Wales. He was an educated lawyer, and was the last native-born Welshman to hold the title Prince of Wales. *Welsh.*

The Jackson Five - The Jackson 5 is an American pop band composed of members of the Jackson family. The group was founded in 1964 in Gary, Indiana, and for most of their career consisted of brothers Jackie, Tito, Jermaine, Marlon and Michael. *Twiddly diddly dee.*

99s - A 99 Flake, 99 or ninety-nine is an ice cream cone with a Cadbury Flake inserted in the ice cream. The term can also refer to the half-sized Cadbury-produced Flake bar, itself specially made for such ice cream cones. **They were 99mm, they are now 66mm. Now that is bloody sneaky.**

Marks and Spencer - Marks and Spencer Group plc (commonly abbreviated to M&S and colloquially known as Marks or Marks & Sparks) is a major British multinational retailer with headquarters in Paddington, London that specialises in selling clothing, beauty, home products and food products. *The change from the old tills came out down a chute. Very exciting as a kid.*

Woolworths - Woolworth (officially Woolworths Group PLC) was a listed British company that owned the High Street retail chain Woolworths. It also owned other companies such as the entertainment distributor Entertainment UK. *Mam worked on the sweet counter; she ate loads. She always carried with her the guilt that this may have contributed to the fact that they went bust.*

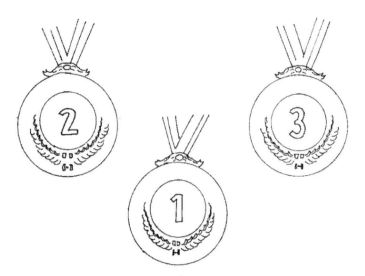

"There is a truth in these stories.
It might not always be the whole truth.
But it is, and always will be,
my truth.
Some names have been changed.
Some characters have been merged to protect the
innocent, and sometimes the guilty.
It is my hope that the ones that remain,
or their loved ones that survive them,
will know who they are."

Lyndon Jeremiah

BA (Hons) (third class, known as a Richard)
Post Graduate Certificate of Education (after resit)
Two A Levels (I started three)
Eleven O levels (prior to girls and alcohol)
Two Welsh College Football Winners Medals
(Not selected for either final)
An 81 point break in Snooker (Jubilee Club, Pontardawe)
Full Driving Licence (after eight attempts)
Life Saving Award (in my pyjamas)
The Minchington Award for Excellence in Craft
Four years full attendance award Catwg Primary School

And many other Medals of Mediocrity...

Acknowledgments

Albert Jeremiah
Professor Angela V John
Jean Foulkes
Wyn Griffiths
Janet Lloyd
Michael Regan
Charlie Thomas
Nathan Shelton
Simon Matthews
Paula Parish
Rebecca Estano
Clare Bell
Jeni Neal
Penny Turnbull

JEREMIAH PUBLISHING
www.jeremiahpublishing.co.uk

Other books by Lyndon Jeremiah

For Children in English and Welsh

Illustrated by Jennie Harmer

Santa's Greatest Secret   978-1-8382713-0-5

Cyfrinach Fwyaf Siôn Corn   978-1-8382713-1-2

Santa's Greatest Love   978-1-8382713-2-9

Cariad Mwyaf Siôn Corn   978-1-8382713-3-6

Illustrated by Nathan Shelton

Four Small Boys from Wales   978-1-8382713-4-3

Pedwar Bachgen Bach o Gymru   978-1-8382713-5-0

Gallant St George and the Dragon of Wales
978-1-8382713-7-4

San y Siôr Dewr a Draig Goch Cymru 978-1-8382713-8-1

Poetry collection

The Man I'm Going to Be   978-0-244-57826-8

JEREMIAH PUBLISHING
www.jeremiahpublishing.co.uk

Printed in Great Britain
by Amazon

29038524R00173